TEACHER'S GUIDE

Connected Mathematics 2 ™

Prime Time

Factors and Multiples

Glenda Lappan
James T. Fey
William M. Fitzgerald
Susan N. Friel
Elizabeth Difanis Phillips

PEARSON

Boston, Massachusetts · Glenview, Illinois · Shoreview, Minnesota · Upper Saddle River, New Jersey

Connected Mathematics™ was developed at Michigan State University with financial support from the Michigan State University Office of the Provost, Computing and Technology, and the College of Natural Science.

This material is based upon work supported by the National Science Foundation under Grant No. MDR 9150217 and Grant No. ESI 9986372. Opinions expressed are those of the authors and not necessarily those of the Foundation.

The Michigan State University authors and administration have agreed that all MSU royalties arising from this publication will be devoted to purposes supported by the Department of Mathematics and the MSU Mathematics Enrichment Fund.

13-digit ISBN 978-0-13-366108-8
10-digit ISBN 0-13-366108-3
2 3 4 5 6 7 8 9 10 11 10 09 08

Authors of Connected Mathematics

(from left to right) Glenda Lappan, Betty Phillips, Susan Friel, Bill Fitzgerald, Jim Fey

Glenda Lappan is a University Distinguished Professor in the Department of Mathematics at Michigan State University. Her research and development interests are in the connected areas of students' learning of mathematics and mathematics teachers' professional growth and change related to the development and enactment of K–12 curriculum materials.

James T. Fey is a Professor of Curriculum and Instruction and Mathematics at the University of Maryland. His consistent professional interest has been development and research focused on curriculum materials that engage middle and high school students in problem-based collaborative investigations of mathematical ideas and their applications.

William M. Fitzgerald (*Deceased*) was a Professor in the Department of Mathematics at Michigan State University. His early research was on the use of concrete materials in supporting student learning and led to the development of teaching materials for laboratory environments. Later he helped develop a teaching model to support student experimentation with mathematics.

Susan N. Friel is a Professor of Mathematics Education in the School of Education at the University of North Carolina at Chapel Hill. Her research interests focus on statistics education for middle-grade students and, more broadly, on teachers' professional development and growth in teaching mathematics K–8.

Elizabeth Difanis Phillips is a Senior Academic Specialist in the Mathematics Department of Michigan State University. She is interested in teaching and learning mathematics for both teachers and students. These interests have led to curriculum and professional development projects at the middle school and high school levels, as well as projects related to the teaching and learning of algebra across the grades.

CMP2 Development Staff

Teacher Collaborator in Residence
Yvonne Grant
Michigan State University

Administrative Assistant
Judith Martus Miller
Michigan State University

Production and Field Site Manager
Lisa Keller
Michigan State University

Technical and Editorial Support
**Brin Keller, Peter Lappan, Jim Laser,
Michael Masterson, Stacey Miceli**

Assessment Team
June Bailey and **Debra Sobko** (Apollo Middle School, Rochester, New York), **George Bright** (University of North Carolina, Greensboro), **Gwen Ranzau Campbell** (Sunrise Park Middle School, White Bear Lake, Minnesota), **Holly DeRosia, Kathy Dole,** and **Teri Keusch** (Portland Middle School, Portland, Michigan), **Mary Beth Schmitt** (Traverse City East Junior High School, Traverse City, Michigan), **Genni Steele** (Central Middle School, White Bear Lake, Minnesota), **Jacqueline Stewart** (Okemos, Michigan), **Elizabeth Tye** (Magnolia Junior High School, Magnolia, Arkansas)

Development Assistants
At Lansing Community College *Undergraduate Assistant:* **James Brinegar**

At Michigan State University *Graduate Assistants:* **Dawn Berk, Emily Bouck, Bulent Buyukbozkirli, Kuo-Liang Chang, Christopher Danielson, Srinivasa Dharmavaram, Deb Johanning, Wesley Kretzschmar, Kelly Rivette, Sarah Sword, Tat Ming Sze, Marie Turini, Jeffrey Wanko;** *Undergraduate Assistants:* **Daniel Briggs, Jeffrey Chapin, Jade Corsé, Elisha Hardy, Alisha Harold, Elizabeth Keusch, Julia Letoutchaia, Karen Loeffler, Brian Oliver, Carl Oliver, Evonne Pedawi, Lauren Rebrovich**

At the University of Maryland *Graduate Assistants:* **Kim Harris Bethea, Kara Karch**

At the University of North Carolina (Chapel Hill) *Graduate Assistants:* **Mark Ellis, Trista Stearns;** *Undergraduate Assistant:* **Daniel Smith**

Advisory Board for CMP2

Thomas Banchoff
Professor of Mathematics
Brown University
Providence, Rhode Island

Anne Bartel
Mathematics Coordinator
Minneapolis Public Schools
Minneapolis, Minnesota

Hyman Bass
Professor of Mathematics
University of Michigan
Ann Arbor, Michigan

Joan Ferrini-Mundy
Associate Dean of the College of
Natural Science; Professor
Michigan State University
East Lansing, Michigan

James Hiebert
Professor
University of Delaware
Newark, Delaware

Susan Hudson Hull
Charles A. Dana Center
University of Texas
Austin, Texas

Michele Luke
Mathematics Curriculum
Coordinator
West Junior High
Minnetonka, Minnesota

Kay McClain
Assistant Professor of
Mathematics Education
Vanderbilt University
Nashville, Tennessee

Edward Silver
Professor; Chair of Educational
Studies
University of Michigan
Ann Arbor, Michigan

Judith Sowder
Professor Emerita
San Diego State University
San Diego, California

Lisa Usher
Mathematics Resource Teacher
California Academy of
Mathematics and Science
San Pedro, California

Field Test Sites for CMP2

During the development of the revised edition of *Connected Mathematics* (CMP2), more than 100 classroom teachers have field-tested materials at 49 school sites in 12 states and the District of Columbia. This classroom testing occurred over three academic years (2001 through 2004), allowing careful study of the effectiveness of each of the 24 units that comprise the program. A special thanks to the students and teachers at these pilot schools.

Arkansas
Magnolia Public Schools
Kittena Bell*, Judith Trowell*; *Central Elementary School:* Maxine Broom, Betty Eddy, Tiffany Fallin, Bonnie Flurry, Carolyn Monk, Elizabeth Tye; *Magnolia Junior High School:* Monique Bryan, Ginger Cook, David Graham, Shelby Lamkin

Colorado
Boulder Public Schools
Nevin Platt Middle School: Judith Koenig

St. Vrain Valley School District, Longmont
Westview Middle School: Colleen Beyer, Kitty Canupp, Ellie Decker*, Peggy McCarthy, Tanya deNobrega, Cindy Payne, Ericka Pilon, Andrew Roberts

District of Columbia
Capitol Hill Day School: Ann Lawrence

Georgia
University of Georgia, Athens
Brad Findell

Madison Public Schools
Morgan County Middle School: Renee Burgdorf, Lynn Harris, Nancy Kurtz, Carolyn Stewart

Maine
Falmouth Public Schools
Falmouth Middle School: Donna Erikson, Joyce Hebert, Paula Hodgkins, Rick Hogan, David Legere, Cynthia Martin, Barbara Stiles, Shawn Towle*

Michigan
Portland Public Schools
Portland Middle School: Mark Braun, Holly DeRosia, Kathy Dole*, Angie Foote, Teri Keusch, Tammi Wardwell

Traverse City Area Public Schools
Bertha Vos Elementary: Kristin Sak; *Central Grade School:* Michelle Clark; Jody Meyers; *Eastern Elementary:* Karrie Tufts; *Interlochen Elementary:* Mary McGee-Cullen; *Long Lake Elementary:* Julie Faulkner*, Charlie Maxbauer, Katherine Sleder; *Norris Elementary:* Hope Slanaker; *Oak Park Elementary:* Jessica Steed; *Traverse Heights Elementary:* Jennifer Wolfert; *Westwoods Elementary:* Nancy Conn; *Old Mission Peninsula School:* Deb Larimer; *Traverse City East Junior High:* Ivanka Berkshire, Ruthanne Kladder, Jan Palkowski, Jane Peterson, Mary Beth Schmitt; *Traverse City West Junior High:* Dan Fouch*, Ray Fouch

Sturgis Public Schools
Sturgis Middle School: Ellen Eisele

Minnesota
Burnsville School District 191
Hidden Valley Elementary: Stephanie Cin, Jane McDevitt

Hopkins School District 270
Alice Smith Elementary: Sandra Cowing, Kathleen Gustafson, Martha Mason, Scott Stillman; *Eisenhower Elementary:* Chad Bellig, Patrick Berger, Nancy Glades, Kye Johnson, Shane Wasserman, Victoria Wilson; *Gatewood Elementary:* Sarah Ham, Julie Kloos, Janine Pung, Larry Wade; *Glen Lake Elementary:* Jacqueline Cramer, Kathy Hering, Cecelia Morris, Robb Trenda; *Katherine Curren Elementary:* Diane Bancroft, Sue DeWit, John Wilson; *L. H. Tanglen Elementary:* Kevin Athmann, Lisa Becker, Mary LaBelle, Kathy Rezac, Roberta Severson; *Meadowbrook Elementary:* Jan Gauger, Hildy Shank, Jessica Zimmerman; *North Junior High:* Laurel Hahn, Kristin Lee, Jodi Markuson, Bruce Mestemacher, Laurel Miller, Bonnie Rinker, Jeannine Salzer, Sarah Shafer, Cam Stottler; *West Junior High:* Alicia Beebe, Kristie Earl, Nobu Fujii, Pam Georgetti, Susan Gilbert, Regina Nelson Johnson, Debra Lindstrom, Michele Luke*, Jon Sorensen

Minneapolis School District 1
Ann Sullivan K–8 School: Bronwyn Collins; Anne Bartel* (Curriculum and Instruction Office)

Wayzata School District 284
Central Middle School: Sarajane Myers, Dan Nielsen, Tanya Ravnholdt

White Bear Lake School District 624
Central Middle School: Amy Jorgenson, Michelle Reich, Brenda Sammon

New York
New York City Public Schools
IS 89: Yelena Aynbinder, Chi-Man Ng, Nina Rapaport, Joel Spengler, Phyllis Tam*, Brent Wyso; *Wagner Middle School:* Jason Appel, Intissar Fernandez, Yee Gee Get, Richard Goldstein, Irving Marcus, Sue Norton, Bernadita Owens, Jennifer Rehn*, Kevin Yuhas

---

* indicates a Field Test Site Coordinator

Ohio

Talawanda School District, Oxford
Talawanda Middle School: Teresa Abrams, Larry Brock, Heather Brosey, Julie Churchman, Monna Even, Karen Fitch, Bob George, Amanda Klee, Pat Meade, Sandy Montgomery, Barbara Sherman, Lauren Steidl

Miami University
Jeffrey Wanko*

Springfield Public Schools
Rockway School: Jim Mamer

Pennsylvania

Pittsburgh Public Schools
Kenneth Labuskes, Marianne O'Connor, Mary Lynn Raith*; *Arthur J. Rooney Middle School:* David Hairston, Stamatina Mousetis, Alfredo Zangaro; *Frick International Studies Academy:* Suzanne Berry, Janet Falkowski, Constance Finseth, Romika Hodge, Frank Machi; *Reizenstein Middle School:* Jeff Baldwin, James Brautigam, Lorena Burnett, Glen Cobbett, Michael Jordan, Margaret Lazur, Tamar McPherson, Melissa Munnell, Holly Neely, Ingrid Reed, Dennis Reft

Texas

Austin Independent School District
Bedichek Middle School: Lisa Brown, Jennifer Glasscock, Vicki Massey

El Paso Independent School District
Cordova Middle School: Armando Aguirre, Anneliesa Durkes, Sylvia Guzman, Pat Holguin*, William Holguin, Nancy Nava, Laura Orozco, Michelle Peña, Roberta Rosen, Patsy Smith, Jeremy Wolf

Plano Independent School District
Patt Henry, James Wohlgehagen*; *Frankford Middle School:* Mandy Baker, Cheryl Butsch, Amy Dudley, Betsy Eshelman, Janet Greene, Cort Haynes, Kathy Letchworth, Kay Marshall, Kelly McCants, Amy Reck, Judy Scott, Syndy Snyder, Lisa Wang; *Wilson Middle School:* Darcie Bane, Amanda Bedenko, Whitney Evans, Tonelli Hatley, Sarah (Becky) Higgs, Kelly Johnston, Rebecca McElligott, Kay Neuse, Cheri Slocum, Kelli Straight

Washington

Evergreen School District
Shahala Middle School: Nicole Abrahamsen, Terry Coon*, Carey Doyle, Sheryl Drechsler, George Gemma, Gina Helland, Amy Hilario, Darla Lidyard, Sean McCarthy, Tilly Meyer, Willow Nuewelt, Todd Parsons, Brian Pederson, Stan Posey, Shawn Scott, Craig Sjoberg, Lynette Sundstrom, Charles Switzer, Luke Youngblood

Wisconsin

Beaver Dam Unified School District
Beaver Dam Middle School: Jim Braemer, Jeanne Frick, Jessica Greatens, Barbara Link, Dennis McCormick, Karen Michels, Nancy Nichols*, Nancy Palm, Shelly Stelsel, Susan Wiggins

---

* indicates a Field Test Site Coordinator

Reviews of CMP to Guide Development of CMP2

Before writing for CMP2 began or field tests were conducted, the first edition of *Connected Mathematics* was submitted to the mathematics faculties of school districts from many parts of the country and to 80 individual reviewers for extensive comments.

School District Survey Reviews of CMP

Arizona
Madison School District #38 (Phoenix)

Arkansas
Cabot School District, Little Rock School District, Magnolia School District

California
Los Angeles Unified School District

Colorado
St. Vrain Valley School District (Longmont)

Florida
Leon County Schools (Tallahassee)

Illinois
School District #21 (Wheeling)

Indiana
Joseph L. Block Junior High (East Chicago)

Kentucky
Fayette County Public Schools (Lexington)

Maine
Selection of Schools

Massachusetts
Selection of Schools

Michigan
Sparta Area Schools

Minnesota
Hopkins School District

Texas
Austin Independent School District, The El Paso Collaborative for Academic Excellence, Plano Independent School District

Wisconsin
Platteville Middle School

Individual Reviewers of CMP

Arkansas
Deborah Cramer; Robby Frizzell *(Taylor)*; Lowell Lynde *(University of Arkansas, Monticello)*; Leigh Manzer *(Norfork)*; Lynne Roberts *(Emerson High School, Emerson)*; Tony Timms *(Cabot Public Schools)*; Judith Trowell *(Arkansas Department of Higher Education)*

California
José Alcantar *(Gilroy)*; Eugenie Belcher *(Gilroy)*; Marian Pasternack *(Lowman M. S. T. Center, North Hollywood)*; Susana Pezoa *(San Jose)*; Todd Rabusin *(Hollister)*; Margaret Siegfried *(Ocala Middle School, San Jose)*; Polly Underwood *(Ocala Middle School, San Jose)*

Colorado
Janeane Golliher *(St. Vrain Valley School District, Longmont)*; Judith Koenig *(Nevin Platt Middle School, Boulder)*

Florida
Paige Loggins *(Swift Creek Middle School, Tallahassee)*

Illinois
Jan Robinson *(School District #21, Wheeling)*

Indiana
Frances Jackson *(Joseph L. Block Junior High, East Chicago)*

Kentucky
Natalee Feese *(Fayette County Public Schools, Lexington)*

Maine
Betsy Berry *(Maine Math & Science Alliance, Augusta)*

Maryland
Joseph Gagnon *(University of Maryland, College Park)*; Paula Maccini *(University of Maryland, College Park)*

Massachusetts
George Cobb *(Mt. Holyoke College, South Hadley)*; Cliff Kanold *(University of Massachusetts, Amherst)*

Michigan
Mary Bouck *(Farwell Area Schools)*; Carol Dorer *(Slauson Middle School, Ann Arbor)*; Carrie Heaney *(Forsythe Middle School, Ann Arbor)*; Ellen Hopkins *(Clague Middle School, Ann Arbor)*; Teri Keusch *(Portland Middle School, Portland)*; Valerie Mills *(Oakland Schools, Waterford)*; Mary Beth Schmitt *(Traverse City East Junior High, Traverse City)*; Jack Smith *(Michigan State University, East Lansing)*; Rebecca Spencer *(Sparta Middle School, Sparta)*; Ann Marie Nicoll Turner *(Tappan Middle School, Ann Arbor)*; Scott Turner *(Scarlett Middle School, Ann Arbor)*

Minnesota
Margarita Alvarez *(Olson Middle School, Minneapolis)*; Jane Amundson *(Nicollet Junior High, Burnsville)*; Anne Bartel *(Minneapolis Public Schools)*; Gwen Ranzau Campbell *(Sunrise Park Middle School, White Bear Lake)*; Stephanie Cin *(Hidden Valley Elementary, Burnsville)*; Joan Garfield *(University of Minnesota, Minneapolis)*; Gretchen Hall *(Richfield Middle School, Richfield)*; Jennifer Larson *(Olson Middle School, Minneapolis)*; Michele Luke *(West Junior High, Minnetonka)*; Jeni Meyer *(Richfield Junior High, Richfield)*; Judy Pfingsten *(Inver Grove Heights Middle School, Inver Grove Heights)*; Sarah Shafer *(North Junior High, Minnetonka)*; Genni Steele *(Central Middle School, White Bear Lake)*; Victoria Wilson *(Eisenhower Elementary, Hopkins)*; Paul Zorn *(St. Olaf College, Northfield)*

New York
Debra Altenau-Bartolino *(Greenwich Village Middle School, New York)*; Doug Clements *(University of Buffalo)*; Francis Curcio *(New York University, New York)*; Christine Dorosh *(Clinton School for Writers, Brooklyn)*; Jennifer Rehn *(East Side Middle School, New York)*; Phyllis Tam *(IS 89 Lab School, New York)*;

Marie Turini *(Louis Armstrong Middle School, New York)*; Lucy West *(Community School District 2, New York)*; Monica Witt *(Simon Baruch Intermediate School 104, New York)*

Pennsylvania
Robert Aglietti *(Pittsburgh)*; Sharon Mihalich *(Freeport)*; Jennifer Plumb *(South Hills Middle School, Pittsburgh)*; Mary Lynn Raith *(Pittsburgh Public Schools)*

Texas
Michelle Bittick *(Austin Independent School District)*; Margaret Cregg *(Plano Independent School District)*; Sheila Cunningham *(Klein Independent School District)*; Judy Hill *(Austin Independent School District)*; Patricia Holguin *(El Paso Independent School District)*; Bonnie McNemar *(Arlington)*; Kay Neuse *(Plano Independent School District)*; Joyce Polanco *(Austin Independent School District)*; Marge Ramirez *(University of Texas at El Paso)*; Pat Rossman *(Baker Campus, Austin)*; Cindy Schimek *(Houston)*; Cynthia Schneider *(Charles A. Dana Center, University of Texas at Austin)*; Uri Treisman *(Charles A. Dana Center, University of Texas at Austin)*; Jacqueline Weilmuenster *(Grapevine-Colleyville Independent School District)*; LuAnn Weynand *(San Antonio)*; Carmen Whitman *(Austin Independent School District)*; James Wohlgehagen *(Plano Independent School District)*

Washington
Ramesh Gangolli *(University of Washington, Seattle)*

Wisconsin
Susan Lamon *(Marquette University, Hales Corner)*; Steve Reinhart *(retired, Chippewa Falls Middle School, Eau Claire)*

Table of Contents

Prime Time
Factors and Multiples

The Student Edition pages for the Unit Opener follow page 15.

Unit Introduction

Prime Time
Factors and Multiples

Goals of the Unit

- Understand relationships among factors, multiples, divisors, and products

- Recognize and use properties of prime and composite numbers, even and odd numbers, and square numbers

- Use rectangles to represent the factor pairs of numbers

- Develop strategies for finding factors and multiples, least common multiples, and greatest common factors

- Recognize and use the fact that every whole number can be written in exactly one way as a product of prime numbers

- Use factors and multiples to solve problems and to explain some numerical facts of everyday life

- Develop a variety of strategies for solving problems—building models, making lists and tables, drawing diagrams, and solving simpler problems

Developing Students' Mathematical Habits

The overall goal of *Connected Mathematics* is to help students develop sound mathematical habits. Through their work in this and other number units, students learn important questions to ask themselves about any situation that can be represented and modeled mathematically, such as:

- *Will breaking a number into factors help me solve the problem?*

- *What relationships are revealed by doing that?*

- *What do the factors and multiples of the numbers tell me about the situation?*

- *How can I find the factors of the numbers?*

- *How can I find the multiples?*

- *What common factors and common multiples do the numbers have?*

Overview

Many important arithmetic problems involve breaking a whole number into equal-size pieces or finding a number into which a given number will divide evenly. Solving problems like these involves finding factors and multiples. For example:

- A class of 30 students is to be divided into equal-size teams for a school competition. What team sizes are possible?

- Frida and Georgia want to go to the art museum together the next time they both have a day off from work. Frida has a day off every fourth day. Georgia has a day off every fifth day. They both had the day off today. In how many days will they be able to go to the museum together?

Solving the first problem involves finding factor pairs of 30. The class can be divided into 1 team of 30, 2 teams of 15, 3 teams of 10, 5 teams of 6, 6 teams of 5, 10 teams of 3, 15 teams of 2, or 30 teams of 1. One of the most curious and important properties of the whole number system is that the answer to this question depends greatly on the number being divided. For example, if the class had just one more student, it could only be divided into 1 team of 31 or 31 teams of 1.

The second problem involves multiples. We need to find the least number of which both 4 and 5 are factors. This number is 20, the least common multiple of 4 and 5. Frida and Georgia can go to the museum together in 20 days.

Solving grouping and repeated-action problems like those above depends on finding factors and multiples of whole numbers. Realizing that some numbers are rich in factors, while other numbers have very few factors, is essential for effective problem solving. A primary goal of this unit is to help students learn some new and useful strategies for finding factors and multiples of whole numbers. They can then apply these strategies to gain familiarity with prime and composite numbers and to solve real-life problems.

Summary of Investigations

Investigation 1

Factors and Products

The Factor Game engages students in a friendly contest in which winning strategies involve distinguishing between numbers with many factors and numbers with few factors. Students are then guided through an analysis of game strategies and introduced to the definitions of *prime numbers* and *composite numbers*. The Applications—Connections—Extensions (ACE) questions are rich in connections to situations in which factors, multiples, and prime numbers are significant.

In the Product Game, students find products of factors. Although students develop strategies to win the game, the focus is on basic multiplication facts. Students then create their own games by selecting factors, determining products, and choosing appropriate dimensions for their game boards.

Investigation 2

Whole-Number Patterns and Relationships

Students make rectangles to represent models for numbers in Problem 2.1. In Question B of Problem 2.1, students use the rectangles they have created to consider how far they must go to be sure that they have found all the factors. You might use the language of the "turn around" point to describe this location where the factors we are finding in pairs give no new factors.

Problem 2.2 encourages conjecturing and creating arguments to support those conjectures. This problem is not essential if time is an issue. It does, however, put students in an environment that allows a conversation about mathematical argument and proof.

Students explore factors and multiples with Venn diagrams in Problem 2.3. The use of Venn diagrams pushes students to begin to notice important things about numbers and their factors and multiples. While Venn diagrams are not a good tool for finding factors and multiples, they are a very good representational device to focus students' attention on the common factors and common multiples of two numbers.

Investigation 3

Common Multiples and Common Factors

Real-life situations are used to motivate student interest in common factors and common multiples. The concepts of least common multiple and greatest common factor, though not formally introduced, are used naturally throughout the problems and in the ACE section. The context of the problems and questions helps make clear whether a solution involves finding a common multiple, a common factor, the least common multiple, or the greatest common factor.

Investigation 4

Factorizations: Searching for Factor Strings

Finding longer and longer factor strings of a number leads students to discover the Fundamental Theorem of Arithmetic: a whole number can be factored into a product of primes in exactly one way, disregarding order. The idea is to help students see that every string shorter than the longest has at least one factor that is not prime. These factors can be broken down further to make a longer string. The process ends when every number in the string is prime and no further breaking down can occur. When you reach this stage, you have the one and only string of primes that can be multiplied together to make the original number—thus arriving at the unique prime factorization of the original number. (Of course, the order in which the prime factors are listed is discounted.) The discussion of why 1 is not a prime number occurs in the ACE section.

Investigation 5

Putting It All Together

This problem is an option that gives students a chance to use a lot of what they have learned in the unit to solve something more challenging. If your time is limited, you might assign the locker problem as extra credit for interested students.

Mathematics Background

Factors and Multiples

Prime Time addresses the basics of number theory: factors, multiples, prime and composite numbers, even and odd numbers, square numbers, greatest common factors, and least common multiples. The concepts of factor and multiple are interdependent. If A is a factor of B, then B is a multiple of A. This means that we can find a number C such that the product of A and C equals B, that is, $A \times C = B$. From this we see that factors always come in pairs. For example, we know that $3 \times 4 = 12$. This says that 3 is a factor of 12 and that 4 is a factor of 12. The two are a factor pair because their product is equal to 12. In fact, there are several statements that can describe the relationships in the number fact $3 \times 4 = 12$. We can say the following:

> 3 is a factor of 12.
> 4 is a factor of 12.
> 3 is a divisor of 12.
> 4 is a divisor of 12.
> 12 is the product of 3 and 4.
> 12 is a multiple of 3.
> 12 is a multiple of 4.
> 12 is divisible by 3.
> 12 is divisible by 4.

It is important that students learn to use this language with meaning. We ask in a number of places for students to write such statements about a given number relationship.

Classifying Numbers by the Sum of the Proper Factors

An *abundant* number is one for which the sum of the proper factors of the number is greater than the number itself. The number 24, for example, is abundant because the sum of its *proper* factors is more than 24. A *deficient* number is one in which the sum of the proper factors is less than the number itself. The number 16 is deficient because the sum of its *proper* factors is less than 16. A perfect number is one in which the sum of the proper factors is equal to the number itself. The number 6 is *perfect* because the sum of its *proper* factors equals 6. Note that 6 and 28 are the only perfect numbers between 1 and 30.

The Multiplicative Identity

Students observe that 1 is a factor of every whole number. The product of 1 and another number, A, is A; that is, $1 \times A = A$. Hence we call the number 1 the *multiplicative identity*. For similar reasons, 0 is the *additive identity*. Zero plus any whole number equals the whole number; that is, $0 + A = A$. These ideas are useful when discussing multiplying and dividing fractions. These are important mathematical ideas that will be discussed in later CMP units.

Finding Near-Perfect Numbers

A near-perfect number is one whose proper factors sum to 1 less than the number itself. For example, the number 4, with proper factors 1 and 2, is near-perfect, because $1 + 2 = 3 = 4 - 1$. The number 16 is near-perfect because $1 + 2 + 4 + 8 = 15 = 16 - 1$.

Near-perfect numbers are useful for finding perfect numbers. Euclid discovered this method:

1. Start with a near-perfect number whose proper factors have a prime sum.

2. Multiply the sum of the factors by the greatest power of 2 less than the sum. The product will be a perfect number.

Examples: The number 4 is near-perfect, and the sum of its proper factors is 3, which is prime. The greatest power of 2 less than 3 is 2, and $3 \times 2 = 6$, which is perfect. The number 8 is also near-perfect, and the sum of its proper factor is 7, which is prime. The greatest power of 2 less than 7 is 4, and $7 \times 4 = 28$, which is perfect. Euclid's method will not work for the near-perfect number 16 because the sum of its proper factors is 15, which is not prime.

Euclid's method always produces even perfect numbers. No one knows whether there are any odd perfect numbers, but we do know that powers of 2 (e.g., 2, 4, 8, 16, 32, etc.) are always near-perfect numbers.

Formal Proofs About Even and Odd Numbers

You might be interested in the formal proof that the sum of two even numbers is even. Any even number y can be written $y = 2n$. Let's take two numbers, $y = 2n$ and $z = 2m$. Then $y + z = 2m + 2n = 2(m + n)$, which is even! The proof that the sum of two odd numbers is even is similar: Any odd number a can be written $a = 2z + 1$. Let's take two odd numbers, $a = 2z + 1$ and $b = 2w + 1$. Then $a + b = 2z + 1 + 2w + 1 = 2z + 2w + 2 = 2(z + w + 1)$, which is even. The same sorts of proofs work for sums of even and odd numbers and the products of even and odd numbers.

The Fundamental Theorem of Arithmetic

Through their work in these investigations, your students discover the Fundamental Theorem of Arithmetic. "Fundamental" theorems are few and far between in mathematics. This implies that the theorem is of "fundamental" importance to mathematics as a field and, in this case, especially to number theory. The Fundamental Theorem of Arithmetic states that every positive whole number can be written as the product of primes in exactly one way, disregarding order. For example, the number 120 can be written as $2 \times 2 \times 2 \times 3 \times 5$. Although you can switch the order of the factors—i.e., you can write $2 \times 3 \times 2 \times 5 \times 2$—every prime product string for 120 will have three 2s, one 3, and one 5. The Fundamental Theorem of Arithmetic helps us to see why 1 is not a prime number. In essence, the theorem states that a whole number can be identified uniquely by its prime factorization. That is, each whole number corresponds to a unique prime factorization, and each prime factorization corresponds to a unique whole number. If 1 were a prime number, this would not be true. Any string of primes could be extended with an unlimited number of 1s. We could say that the "prime" factorization of 12 is $3 \times 2 \times 2$ or $3 \times 2 \times 2 \times 1$ or $3 \times 2 \times 2 \times 1 \times 1 \times 1 \times 1 \times 1 \times 1 \times 1 \times 1$. From this, we see that we can express 12 as a product using as factors as many 1's as we like.

Common Factors and Common Multiples

We introduce Venn diagrams as a way of focusing students' attention on common factors or multiples of two numbers. The following are two of the Venn diagram problems in Investigation 2 with all numbers less than or equal to 50 placed in their appropriate place. We do not ask students to fill in all the numbers that fall outside the areas of the circles, but we do ask in some cases for them to fill in some that would fall outside.

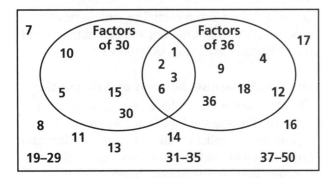

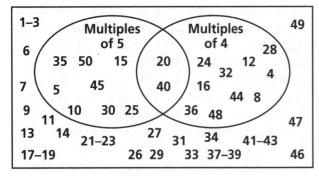

As you can see, the Venn diagrams highlight the areas of overlap. In the first diagram you can see the common factors of the numbers. In the second diagram you can see some common multiples. This allows you to ask questions about what other numbers would be in the overlap if you kept checking numbers into the hundreds. In the case of common factors, no additional numbers would be added to the overlap (intersection). However, for common multiples there would be a never-ending stream of numbers we could add to the intersection—every multiple of 20 will be in the intersection.

The Least Common Multiple

If the two numbers have no common factors other than 1, then the least common multiple will be the product of the two numbers. ($13 \times 17 = 221$)

If the two numbers have a common factor, the least common multiple will be the product of the two numbers divided by the greatest common factor. ($12 \times 14 \div 2 = 84$, so 84 is the least common multiple.)

The Relationship of Factor Pairs to the Square Root of the Number

An important question arises naturally out of the investigation of rectangles one can make from a fixed number of tiles: How do I know when I have all the rectangles possible except for orientation? Another form of the question is: How do I find the "turn around" point in listing all the factor pairs of a number? A more sophisticated version of the question is: What numbers do I have to check to find all the factors of a number or to show that it is prime?

The key to finding all the factors of a given number, n, is to examine systematically the whole numbers that are less than or equal to the square root of n. Your students probably have little understanding of square roots at this stage, so they are more likely to see that the turn around occurs when the factors in the pairs get very close together. If we look at the factor pairs for 24 we see:

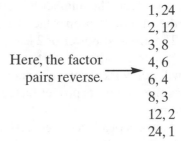

Students begin to see that the 4×6 rectangle is the most square-like of the rectangles. They also notice that as one edge of a rectangle for 24 gets longer, the other edge gets shorter. This also implies that at some point the numbers in the column on the left get larger than the numbers in the column on the right. Where the order of size of edges changes is the turn around point.

Another way students have to see the turn around point is geometrically. By superimposing the rectangles for a number on top of each other in order, you can see the symmetry around the turn around point.

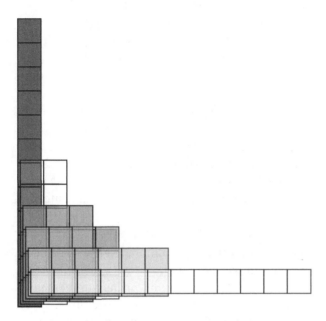

When the rectangles from factor pairs get as close to a square as possible, you have reached the turn around point and have found all the factors. When the number is a square number, you actually hit the turn around point with the rectangle that is a square. The length of the side of that square is the square root of the original number and the turn around point.

All the questions posed at the beginning depend ultimately on understanding that for any number, the two factors in a factor pair lie on opposite sides of the square root of the number. For example, analyze the factors and their pairings for 30 and 36.

The factors of 30 are:
1, 2, 3, 5, 6, 10, 15, 30.
The factors of 36 are:
1, 2, 3, 4, 6, 9, 12, 18, 36.

If we draw lines connecting the factor pairs in each, we get the following:

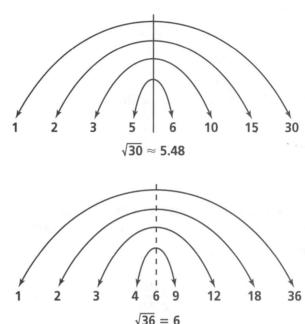

From the diagrams you can see that the square root becomes like a fulcrum around which factor pairs array themselves. We expect that your students will see that the pair of factors that make the most square-like rectangle indicates the place after which the factor pairs reverse and repeat themselves. Later in the unit when the students are finding the prime factorization of numbers, the answer to the question of how far one has to check to be sure a number is either prime or to find all of its prime factors is, once again, the square root. If you check all the prime numbers less than the square root, you will have found all the smaller prime factors of each factor pair involving a prime. If you find no such prime factors, then you can conclude that the number is prime.

Finding Prime Factorizations
Another way to find the prime factorization of a number is to use a recording mechanism to help you keep track of the prime factors you have already found. In the Student Edition we suggest the following recording scheme with the example of the prime factorization of 100 given:

First, find one prime factor of 100. Start with 2, the least prime that divides 100. Divide 100 by 2, showing the work as an upside-down division problem.

$$2 \overline{\smash{\big)}\ 100}$$
$$50$$

Next, find a prime factor of 50. You can use 2 again. Add another "step" to the division problem.

$$2 \overline{\smash{\big)}\ 100}$$
$$2 \overline{\smash{\big)}\ 50}$$
$$25$$

Now, find a prime factor of 25. The only possibility is 5. Add a third "step" to the division problem.

$$2 \overline{\smash{\big)}\ 100}$$
$$2 \overline{\smash{\big)}\ 50}$$
$$5 \overline{\smash{\big)}\ 25}$$
$$5$$

You are left with a prime number, 5. From the final diagram, you can read the prime factorization of 100: $100 = 2 \times 2 \times 5 \times 5$.

In the Teacher's Guide, we give another way to find the longest factorization of a number. This method is to make a factor tree. This method is useful because it suggests "breaking apart" numbers into their factor pairs and subsequently "breaking apart" the factors. Below we show this method for 360.

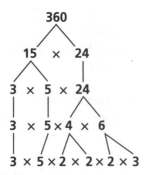

Students might develop a similar method on their own. If some students are having difficulty finding the longest (prime) factorization of a number, you might want to lead them to this method. The methods are equally valid, so students should use the one that makes the most sense to them.

Classifying the Number 1

The question of how to classify and use the number 1 arises in many circumstances. Mathematicians want to write whole numbers in terms of a *unique* factorization. If 1 were a prime number, we could make any string longer by multiplying by 1. The number 14 could be written 7×2 or $7 \times 2 \times 1$ or $7 \times 2 \times 1 \times 1 \times 1$. In addition, calling 1 a prime number violates the definition of "prime number." The Fundamental Theorem of Arithmetic is a theorem about factorization into primes, so we don't want to consider the number 1 as a prime. We cannot consider it composite, as it is not the product of two or more different whole numbers. Thus the number 1 is in a classification by itself. It is called the "unit" and is neither prime nor composite.

Finding Greater Prime Numbers

We know that the prime numbers grow sparser and sparser as whole numbers get greater, but is it possible that at some point prime numbers just "run out"? The answer is no: suppose there were a "greatest" prime number. Let's say there were k prime numbers in total. Suppose we label all of the primes: $n_1, n_2, n_3, \ldots$, and so on. So we would say $n_1 = 2, n_2 = 3, n_3 = 5, n_4 = 7$. We would eventually get up to n_k. Now let's look at the product of all of those primes: $n_1 \times n_2 \times n_3 \times \ldots \times n_k$. Of course this number isn't prime. But what happens if we add 1? Let's look at $n_1 \times n_2 \times n_3 \times \ldots \times n_k + 1$. Whatever prime number we choose can't divide *this* number evenly because the remainder when we divide will always be 1! And remember, we've supposed that *every* prime is included in this list. So, this number is prime! But it must be greater than n_k, which means that our original supposition that there is a "greatest prime" is wrong. There cannot be a greatest prime.

Large prime numbers are important in coding systems for transmitting secret information. The Electronic Frontier Foundation awarded Nayan Hajratwala of Plymouth, Michigan, $50,000 for finding a prime number with more than 2 million digits! He found the prime number in 1999 on his personal computer. He let the computer look for the prime number during idle time, and it took 111 days. We would write down the number for you, but in this type, it would be more than 2 miles long. The recent work (August 2002) by

Dr. Manindra Agrawal and two college students, Neeraj Kayal and Nitin Saxena, has made finding large primes much easier. A 7,235,733-digit prime number was found in May 2004.

The book *The Mathematical Tourist* by Ivars Peterson has a fascinating chapter called "Prime Pursuits" that might interest students.

Using Prime Factorizations to Find the Greatest Common Factor and the Least Common Multiple

Once you have the prime factorizations you can use them to find the greatest common factor (GCF) and the least common multiple (LCM). Here is an example:

$$72 = 2 \times 2 \times 2 \times 3 \times 3$$

$$120 = 2 \times 2 \times 2 \times 3 \times 5$$

The prime factors that the two numbers have in common are 2, 2, 2, and 3. To find the greatest common factor we can multiply these numbers to get $2 \times 2 \times 2 \times 3 = 24$. Thus, 24 divides each of the original numbers and no larger number does so.

The least common multiple can be found by taking the union of all the prime factors. This means that you take the part in common and multiply that by each of the prime factors that are not in common. So the LCM of 72 and 120 is $2 \times 2 \times 2 \times 3 \times 3 \times 5 = 360$.

We do ask the students to find some numbers whose least common multiple is the same as the product of the two numbers. Examples are 72 and 35. If you look at the prime factorization of these two, they have no primes in common. Such numbers are **relatively prime**. They have no common factors other than 1. In such a case, the least common multiple is the product of the two numbers, in this case $72 \times 35 = 2,520$. If you used the same strategy as above, you would have multiplied the prime factorization of 72 by the prime factorization of 35. This is $2 \times 2 \times 2 \times 3 \times 3 \times 5 \times 7 = 2,520$.

The Relationship Between the Greatest Common Factor and the Least Common Multiple

You can analyze the makeup of the least common multiple in another way.

The product of 72 and 120 is:
$2 \times 2 \times 2 \times 3 \times 3 \times 2 \times 2 \times 2 \times 3 \times 5 = 8,640$.

You can see each of the prime factorizations of the two numbers in this product.

| 72 | × | 120 | = 8,640 |

$(2 \times 2 \times 2 \times 3 \times 3) \times (2 \times 2 \times 2 \times 3 \times 5) = 8,640$

Circle the GCF and the LCM of the two numbers.

GCF = 24   LCM = 360

$(2 \times 2 \times 2 \times 3) \times (3 \times 2 \times 2 \times 2 \times 3 \times 5) = 8,640$

So, GCF(72, 120) × LCM(72, 120) = 72 × 120, or   24   ×   360   =   8,640.

We can solve this equation to find a rule for finding the LCM.

$$\text{GCF}(72, 120) \times \text{LCM}(72, 120) = 72 \times 120$$
$$\text{LCM}(72, 120) = \frac{72 \times 120}{\text{GCF}(72, 120)}$$

In general, $\text{LCM}(a, b) = \frac{a \times b}{\text{GCF}(a, b)}$.

Applied Problems

Another feature of this unit is the set of applied problems that engage the students in using their knowledge of primes, factors, multiples, factor pairs, and square numbers. These problems also create situations where the students have to figure out which of the several things they have learned to do is appropriate to help solve the problem. Gaining experience in selecting what is needed from among one's mathematical tools is critical for students if we expect them to be able to make use of what they know. Investigations 3 and 5 are devoted to creating such experiences.

Big Idea	Prior Work	Future Work
Determining the factors of whole numbers; finding the greatest common factor of two numbers	Learning and applying multiplication and division facts; applying the division algorithm (elementary school)	Performing arithmetic operations with fractions (*Bits and Pieces I, II & III*); comparing, scaling, and testing for similarity (*Stretching and Shrinking, Comparing and Scaling*); factoring algebraic expressions (*Frogs, Fleas, and Painted Cubes; Say It With Symbols; The Shapes of Algebra*)
Generating multiples of numbers; finding the least common multiple of two numbers	Learning and applying multiplication facts; counting by 2's, 3's, etc. (elementary school)	Understanding decimal numbers and the concept of place value (*Bits and Pieces I, II, & III; Comparing and Scaling*); identifying and analyzing patterns in the products of two numbers (*Covering and Surrounding; Variables and Patterns; Moving Straight Ahead; The Shapes of Algebra*)
Determining factorizations, including the prime factorization, of a whole number	Learning and applying multiplication and division facts; testing numbers for divisibility (elementary school)	Finding the LCM in order to find common denominators for fractions and ratios (*Bits and Pieces I, II, & III; Comparing and Scaling*); studying patterns in multiplicative relationships to develop algorithms for finding area, surface area, and volume of figures (*Covering and Surrounding*); identifying irrational numbers (*Looking for Pythagoras*); studying exponential relationships (*Growing, Growing, Growing*); developing and applying counting strategies (*Clever Counting © 2004*)
Classifying numbers as prime or composite, as even or odd, and as abundant, deficient, or perfect	Applying multiplication, addition, and division facts; comparing positive whole numbers (elementary school)	Classifying numbers as positive or negative (*Accentuate the Negative*) and as rational or irrational (*Looking for Pythagoras*); classifying relationships as linear, quadratic, inverse, or exponential (*Variables and Patterns; Moving Straight Ahead; Thinking with Mathematical Models; Growing, Growing, Growing; The Shapes of Algebra*)

Planning for the Unit

Pacing Suggestions and Materials

Investigations and Assessments	Pacing 45–50 min. classes	Materials for Students	Materials for Teachers
1 Factors and Products	4 days	Colored pens, pencils, or markers; Labsheets 1.1 and 1.3 (1 of each per pair); Labsheet 1.2 (1 per student); paper clips (2 per pair); colored chips (about 12 of each of 2 colors per pair)	Transparencies 1.1A–1.1D, 1.2, 1.3A–1.3C; 2 paper clips
Mathematical Reflections	$\frac{1}{2}$ day		
Assessment: Check Up 1	$\frac{1}{2}$ day		
2 Whole-Numbers Patterns and Relationships	3 days	Colored pens, pencils, or markers; square tiles (30 per pair); grid paper; blank sheets of paper; scissors; tape; Labsheets 2.3A and 2.3B (1 of each per pair)	Models for odd and even numbers; Transparencies 2.1, 2.2, 2.3A–2.3C
Mathematical Reflections	$\frac{1}{2}$ day		
3 Common Multiples and Common Factors	4 days		Transparency 3.4
Mathematical Reflections	$\frac{1}{2}$ day		
Assessment: Check Up 2	$\frac{1}{2}$ day		
4 Factorizations	3 days	Colored pens, pencils, or markers; Labsheet 4.1	Transparencies 4.1A, 4.1B, 4.2, 4.3
Mathematical Reflections	$\frac{1}{2}$ day		
Assessment: Partner Quiz	1 day		
5 Putting It All Together (optional)	2 days	Colored pens, pencils, or markers; grid paper; two-color chips or other similar manipulatives; Labsheets 5.1A and 5.1B	Transparencies 5.1, 5ACE Exercise 25
Mathematical Reflections	$\frac{1}{2}$ day		
Looking Back and Looking Ahead	$\frac{1}{2}$ day		
Assessment: Unit Project	Optional		
Assessment: Self-Assessment	Take Home		
Assessment: Unit Test	1 day		

Total Time	**22 days**	**Materials for Use in All Investigations**	
For detailed pacing for Problems within each Investigation, see the Suggested Pacing at the beginning of each Investigation.		Calculators, blank transparencies and transparency markers (optional), student notebooks	Blank transparencies and transparency markers (optional)

For pacing with block scheduling, see next page.

Pacing for Block Scheduling (90-minute class periods)

Investigation	Suggested Pacing	Investigation	Suggested Pacing	Investigation	Suggested Pacing
Investigation 1	**3 days**	**Investigation 3**	**$2\frac{1}{2}$ days**	**Investigation 5**	**$1\frac{1}{2}$ days**
Problem 1.1	1 day	Problem 3.1	$\frac{1}{2}$ day	Problem 5.1	1 day
Problem 1.2	$\frac{1}{2}$ day	Problem 3.2	$\frac{1}{2}$ day	Math Reflections	$\frac{1}{2}$ day
Problem 1.3	1 day	Problem 3.3	$\frac{1}{2}$ day		
Math Reflections	$\frac{1}{2}$ day	Problem 3.4	$\frac{1}{2}$ day		
Investigation 2	**2 days**	Math Reflections	$\frac{1}{2}$ day		
Problem 2.1	$\frac{1}{2}$ day	**Investigation 4**	**2 days**		
Problem 2.2	$\frac{1}{2}$ day	Problem 4.1	$\frac{1}{2}$ day		
Problem 2.3	$\frac{1}{2}$ day	Problem 4.2	$\frac{1}{2}$ day		
Math Reflections	$\frac{1}{2}$ day	Problem 4.3	$\frac{1}{2}$ day		
		Math Reflections	$\frac{1}{2}$ day		

Vocabulary

Essential Terms Developed in This Unit		Useful Terms Referenced in This Unit
common factor	factorization	abundant number
common multiple	greatest common factor (GCF)	adjacent primes
composite number	least common multiple (LCM)	deficient number
conjecture	multiple	divisible by
dimensions	odd number	distinct
(whole number) divisor	prime factorization	Fundamental Theorem of Arithmetic
even number	prime number	intersection
exponent	proper factor	near-perfect number
(whole number) factor	square number	perfect number
factor pair	Venn diagram	relatively prime
		twin primes

Program Resources

Go Online
PHSchool.com
For: Teacher Resources
Web Code: amk-5500

INTRODUCTION

Components

Use the chart below to quickly see which components are available for each Investigation.

Investigation	Labsheets	Additional Practice	Transparencies		Formal Assessment		Assessment Options	
			Problem	Summary	Check Up	Partner Quiz	Multiple-Choice	Question Bank
1	1.1, 1.2, 1.3	✔	1.1A–C, 1.3A, 1.3B	1.1D, 1.2, 1.3C	✔		✔	✔
2	2.3A, 2.3B	✔	2.1, 2.2, 2.3A, 2.3B	2.3C			✔	✔
3		✔		3.4	✔		✔	✔
4	4.1	✔	4.1A, 4.1B, 4.2, 4.3			✔	✔	✔
5	5.1A, 5.1B	✔	5.1, 5ACE Exercise 25				✔	✔
Unit Project								
For the Unit		*ExamView* CD-ROM, Web site			Unit Test, Unit Project, Notebook Check, Self-Assessment		Multiple-Choice, Question Bank, *ExamView* CD-ROM	

Also Available for Use With This Unit

• Parent Guide: take-home brochure for the unit

• Implementing CMP • Spanish Assessment Resources
• Additional online and technology resources

Technology

The Use of Calculators

Connected Mathematics was developed with the belief that calculators should be available and that students should learn when their use is appropriate. For this reason, we do not designate specific problems as "calculator problems." The calculations in *Prime Time* involve only simple arithmetic, so nonscientific calculators are adequate.

Student Interactivity CD-ROM

Includes interactive versions of the Factor Game, Product Game, and Locker Problem. Also available online at PHSchool.com, Web Code amk-5500.

PHSchool.com

For Students Multiple-choice practice with instant feedback, updated data sources, data sets for Tinkerplots data software.
For Teachers Professional development, curriculum support, downloadable forms, and more.

See also www.math.msu.edu/cmp for more resources for both teachers and students.

ExamView® CD-ROM

Create multiple versions of practice sheets and tests for course objectives and standardized tests. Includes dynamic questions, online testing, student reports, and all test and practice items in Spanish. Also includes all items in the Assessment Resources and Additional Practice.

Teacher Express™ CD-ROM

Includes a lesson planning tool, the Teacher's Guide pages, and all the teaching resources.

LessonLab Online Courses

LessonLab offers comprehensive, facilitated professional development designed to help teachers implement CMP and improve student achievement. To learn more, please visit PHSchool.com/cmp2.

Assessment Summary

Ongoing Informal Assessment

Embedded in the Student Unit

Problems Use students' work from the Problems to informally check student understanding.

ACE exercises Use ACE exercises for homework assignments to assess student understanding.

Mathematical Reflections Have students summarize their learning at the end of each Investigation.

Looking Back and Looking Ahead At the end of the unit, use the first two sections to allow students to show what they know about the unit.

Additional Resources

Teacher's Edition Use the Check for Understanding feature of some Summaries and the probing questions that appear in the *Launch, Explore,* or *Summarize* sections of all Investigations to check student understanding.

Summary Transparencies Use these transparencies to focus class attention on a summary check for understanding.

Self Assessment

Notebook Check Students use this tool to organize and check their notebooks before giving them to their teacher. Located in *Assessment Resources.*

Self Assessment At the end of the unit, students reflect on and provide examples of what they learned. Located in *Assessment Resources.*

Formal Assessment

Choose the assessment materials that are appropriate for your students.

Assessment	For Use After	Focus	Student Work
Check Up 1	Invest. 1	Skills	Individual
Check Up 2	Invest. 3	Skills	Individual
Partner Quiz	Invest. 4	Rich problems	Pair
Unit Test	The Unit	Skills, rich problems	Individual
Unit Project	The Unit	Rich problems	Individual

Additional Resources

Multiple-Choice Items Use these items for homework, review, a quiz, or add them to the Unit Test.

Question Bank Choose from these questions for homework, review, or replacements for Quiz, Check Up, or Unit Test questions.

Additional Practice Choose practice exercises for each investigation for homework, review, or formal assessments.

ExamView **CD-ROM** Create practice sheets, review quizzes, and tests with this dynamic software. Give online tests and receive student progress reports. *(All test items are also available in Spanish.)*

Spanish Assessment Resources

Includes Partner Quizzes, Check Ups, Unit Test, Multiple-Choice Items, Question Bank, Notebook Check, and Self-Assessment. Plus, the *ExamView* CD-ROM has all test items in Spanish.

Correlation to Standardized Tests

Investigation	NAEP	Terra Nova				Local Test
		CAT6	CTBS	ITBS	SAT10	
1 Factors and Products	N5b, N5c, N5d	✔		✔	✔	
2 Whole-Number Patterns and Relationships	N5a, N5b, N5f	✔		✔		
3 Common Multiples and Common Factors	N5b, N5c, N5f	✔				
4 Factorizations: Searching for Factor Strings	N5b, N5d	✔			✔	
5 Putting It All Together	N5b, N5f	✔		✔	✔	

NAEP National Assessment of Educational Progress

CAT6/Terra Nova California Achievement Test, 6th Ed.
CTBS/Terra Nova Comprehensive Test of Basic Skills

ITBS Iowa Test of Basic Skills, Form M
SAT10 Stanford Achievement Test, 10th Ed.

Using the Unit Opener

One way to introduce *Prime Time* is to ask your students to brainstorm about the ways they use numbers every day. Tell your students that in *Prime Time*, they will study whole numbers.

Explain that there are important and interesting questions that involve whole numbers. Refer students to the three questions posed on the opening page of the Student Edition. You may want to have a class discussion about these questions, but do not worry about finding the "correct" answers at this time. Take a few minutes to allow ideas from the students with the goal of generating enthusiasm for the kinds of situations in the unit. The questions serve as an advanced organizer for what the students will encounter and learn to do during the unit. Each question is posed again in the investigations, at the time when the students have learned the mathematical concepts required to answer it. Ask your students to keep these questions in mind as they work through the investigations and to think about how they might use the ideas they are learning to help them determine the answers.

After you discuss the questions, introduce students to the unit project.

You can use the unit goals to help the students to anticipate what is coming up in the unit and to build a set of expectations for the work of the students.

Introducing the Unit Project

An optional assessment item for *Prime Time* is the My Special Number project. Here students are asked to choose a number between 10 and 100 and to write several things they already know about it. Students can then work with their special number throughout the unit. In each Mathematical Reflections, students are prompted to add more information about their special number in their notebooks. At the end of the unit, students are asked to create projects highlighting their numbers.

Give the students some time structure to help them know what you expect on the project and when it is due. For example, you might decide to assign choosing a special number and doing the notebook writing as a part of the first homework.

In addition, you may want to set aside a few minutes of class time for students to write about their numbers. Some teachers have found it useful to have students designate one or two "special number pages" in their notebooks to record information about their numbers.

See the Guide to the Unit Project section on page 105 for more information about assigning and assessing the project. There you will find a rubric and samples of student projects. Each sample is followed by a teacher's comments about assessing the project.

Using the Mathematical Highlights

The Mathematical Highlights page in the student edition provides information to students, parents, and other family members. It gives students a preview of the mathematics and some of the overarching questions that they should ask themselves while studying *Prime Time*.

As they work through the unit, students can refer back to the Mathematical Highlights page to review what they have learned and to preview what is still to come. This page also tells students' families what mathematical ideas and activities will be covered as the class works through *Prime Time*.

Reference Resources for the Unit

For Students

Henry, Boyd. *Every Number Is Special*. Palo Alto, Calif.: Dale Seymour Publications, 1985.

Peterson, Ivars. *The Mathematical Tourist: Snapshots of Modern Mathematics*. New York: W. H. Freeman and Co., 1988.

Wells, David. *The Penguin Dictionary of Curious and Interesting Numbers*. New York: Penguin Books, 1986.

For Teachers

Bezuszka, Stanley and Margaret Kenney. *Number Treasury*. Palo Alto, Calif.: Dale Seymour Publications, 1982.

Prime Time

Factors and Multiples

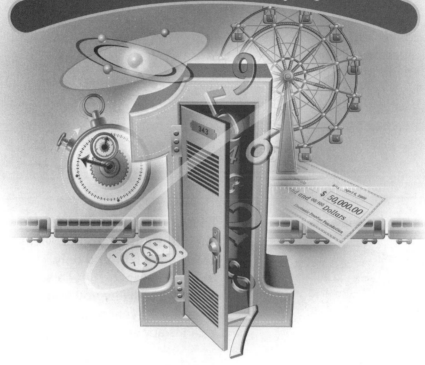

Glenda Lappan
James T. Fey
William M. Fitzgerald
Susan N. Friel
Elizabeth Difanis Phillips

PEARSON

Boston, Massachusetts · Glenview, Illinois · Shoreview, Minnesota · Upper Saddle River, New Jersey

STUDENT PAGE

Notes _____

_____

_____

_____

Prime Time

Factors and Multiples

Why is it convenient to measure time using 60 minutes in an hour (not 59 or 61) and 24 hours in a day (not 23 or 25)?

Insects called cicadas (si KAY dahs) spend most of their lives underground. Many come above ground only every 13 years or 17 years. Why is it unlikely you will ever see 13-year and 17-year cicadas appear together?

Why does your birthday fall on a different day of the week from one year to the next? Why is the same also true for New Year's Day and the Fourth of July?

Notes _____

_____

_____

_____

Think for a minute about some of the ways in which you use numbers. You use numbers to count, to measure, to make comparisons, and to describe where places are located. Numbers help you communicate, find information, use technology, and make purchases. Numbers can also help you think about situations such as those on the previous page.

Whole numbers have interesting properties and structures you may not have thought about. For example, some numbers can be divided evenly by many numbers, while others can be divided evenly by only a few numbers. Some pairs of numbers have lots of factors in common, while others share only one factor. The investigations in *Prime Time* will help you learn to use ideas about the structure of numbers to explain some curious patterns, to solve problems, and to think about some interesting questions, such as those on the previous page.

Notes _____

_____

_____

_____

Mathematical Highlights

Factors and Multiples

In *Prime Time,* you will explore important properties of whole numbers, especially properties related to multiplication and division.

You will learn how to

- Understand relationships among factors, multiples, divisors, and products
- Recognize and use properties of prime and composite numbers, even and odd numbers, and square numbers
- Use rectangles to represent the factor pairs of numbers
- Develop strategies for finding factors and multiples, least common multiples, and greatest common factors
- Recognize and use the fact that every whole number can be written in exactly one way as a product of prime numbers
- Use factors and multiples to solve problems and to explain some numerical facts of everyday life
- Develop a variety of strategies for solving problems—building models, making lists and tables, drawing diagrams, and solving simpler problems

When you encounter a new math problem, ask yourself questions about the numbers and relationships involved in the problem. In this unit, you might ask questions such as these:

Will breaking a number into factors help me solve the problem?

What relationships will doing that help me see?

What do the factors and multiples of the numbers tell me about the situation?

How can I find the factors of the numbers?

How can I find the multiples?

What common factors and common multiples do the numbers have?

4 Prime Time

Notes _____

_____

_____

_____

Unit Project

My Special Number

Many people have a number that they think is interesting. Choose a whole number between 10 and 100 that you especially like.

In your notebook:

• record your number

• explain why you chose that number

• list three or four mathematical facts about your number

• list three or four connections you can make between your number and your world

As you work through the investigations in *Prime Time*, you will learn a lot about numbers. Think about how these new ideas apply to your special number. Add any new information about your number to your notebook. You may want to designate one or two "special-number" pages in your notebook, to record this information. At the end of the unit, your teacher will ask you to find an interesting way to report to the class about your special number.

Unit Project My Special Number 5

Notes _____

_____

_____

_____

Investigation 1 · Factors and Products

Mathematical and Problem-Solving Goals

- Become familiar with the factors of the numbers from 2 to 30
- Review multiplication and division facts
- Relate dividing and finding factors of a number
- Classify numbers as prime or composite
- Recognize that some numbers are rich in factors, while others have few factors
- Develop understanding of factors and multiples and the relationships between them
- Understand that some products are the result of more than one factor pair (for example, $18 = 9 \times 2$ and $18 = 6 \times 3$)

Summary of Problems

Problem 1.1 · Playing the Factor Game

Students start with a number and find its factors. Winning strategies involve recognizing the difference between prime numbers and composite numbers.

Problem 1.2 · Playing to Win the Factor Game

Students analyze Factor Game strategies and are introduced to the definitions of prime and composite numbers.

Problem 1.3 · The Product Game

Students start with one factor and mentally try various possibilities in choosing a factor to go with the fixed factor to make a product that gives a useful space on the game board.

A Note on Calculators

In the Connected Mathematics curriculum, we assume that students have access to calculators at all times. However, we hope that students will develop good estimation and mental arithmetic skills. This means that you need to give your students guidelines about the appropriate uses of calculators. In some classes, students may be ready to do all the arithmetic in the Factor Game without the help of calculators. In other classes, students may need to use calculators to check their mental computations. Use your judgment about whether to use the game as an opportunity for practice in mental arithmetic or to encourage your students to use calculators. After students have a sense of the Factor Game, you may find it appropriate to encourage them to use calculators to keep running totals of their scores.

	Suggested Pacing	Materials for Students	Materials for Teachers	ACE Assignments
All	$4\frac{1}{2}$ days	Calculators; colored pens, pencils or markers; blank transparencies and transparency markers (optional: for recording results); student notebooks	Blank transparencies and transparency markers	
1.1	$1\frac{1}{2}$ days	Labsheet 1.1 (1 per pair)	Transparencies 1.1A–1.1D	1–7, 28–31, 39
1.2	1 day	Labsheet 1.2 (1 per student; optional)	Transparency 1.2	8–16, 32–34, 40–44
1.3	$1\frac{1}{2}$ days	Labsheet 1.3 (1 per pair), paper clips (2 per pair), colored chips (12 each of 2 colors per pair)	Transparencies 1.3A–1.3C; 2 paper clips	17–27, 35–38, 45–49
MR	$\frac{1}{2}$ day			

1.1 Playing the Factor Game

Goals

- Become familiar with the factors of the numbers from 2 to 30
- Review multiplication and division of small whole numbers
- Begin to recognize the difference between prime numbers and composite numbers
- Relate dividing and finding factors of a number

This section provides students an opportunity to learn about factors by playing a two-person board game. On each turn, one player chooses a number, and the other player finds the factors of that number. While playing the game, students become familiar with the factors of the numbers from 2 to 30 and review multiplication and division of small whole numbers.

Launch 1.1

Discuss a couple of examples of what a factor of a number is. (Some are given in the student edition in the introductory paragraph for the investigation.) Remind students that there are two ways to think of a factor: as one of the numbers that is multiplied to get a product, and as a divisor of a number.

Suggested Questions You could ask students to give examples:

- *What factors can you multiply to get a product of 10?*
- *What numbers divide 10 evenly?*
- *How are these two lists related?*

When you feel your students understand what a factor is, introduce the Factor Game. The rules for the game and part of a sample game are given in the student edition, but the best way to get students started is to play a game against the class using the game board on Transparency 1.1A. Rather than reading all the rules at the start, explain the rules as the need arises during the game. When you play against the class, we suggest that you take your turn first and that you choose a non-prime number, such as 26, for your first move.

This way, students can discover the power of a prime first move. Have students play the game two or three times with a partner. You may wish to laminate game boards for repeated use.

Explore 1.1

Look for interesting strategies or observations that students are making. For example, some pairs kept running differences between their scores rather than a total for each. When asked why, they said it helped them select a number that would narrow the difference if you were losing or increase the difference if you were winning.

Suggested Questions As you move around, if students are ready, you could have them think about the following questions:

- *Is it better to go first or second? Why?*
- *What is the best first move? Why?*
- *How do you know when the game is over?*
- *How do you know when you have found all the factors of a number?*

Going Further

Be sure to address these questions in summary. You could write them on the board.

- *Is there a way to have all the numbers circled on the game board?*
- *What is the fewest number of factors that can be circled in a finished game?*
- *What is the worst first move? Is there only one possibility?*

Summarize 1.1

Suggested Questions You may want to have a few students share some ideas they discovered while playing the game. Then discuss the four questions asked in the Explore:

- *Is it better to go first or second? Why?*
- *What is the best first move? Why?*
- *How do you know when the game is over?*

- *How do you know when you have found all the factors of a number?*

Summary Transparency 1.1D

To push students to think a bit more about factors, use the situations and questions that are posed on Summary Transparency 1.1D:

1. *What do you think is a good strategy for playing the Factor Game?* (A good strategy is to start with those numbers that have only two factors: the number itself and 1. For that move, your opponent scores only 1 point. I would choose a large such number, since that would give me many points and my opponent only one point. After the first move, such a number is not a good choice, because you lose a turn and do not score, because the only proper factor, 1, would have been circled no matter what first move your opponent made. After that, careful choices of numbers with several factors are good.)

Here are Cam's and Liza's strategies:

Cam *Bigger numbers must have more factors than smaller numbers, so I always try to circle small numbers on my turn. That way my opponent won't get very many points.*

Liza *Some numbers don't have any factors except 1 and themselves. I try to choose those numbers so my opponent gets only one point.*

2. *Do you think their strategies are good ones?* (Cam's strategy is flawed because he will not get very many points himself. For example, if he chooses 2 for a first move, he gets two points and his opponent gets 1. He could have chosen 29 and his opponent would still get 1 point but he would get 29. Also, he might consider 6 a "small" number, but he and his opponent will both get 6 points. Liza's strategy is flawed because she will keep losing a turn after the first turn.)

Include students' first descriptions of *factors* and *divisors* in the vocabulary section of their notebooks.

Since Problem 1.2 is an analysis of the game, you can delay an extensive summary until then. This summary will lead naturally into the launch of the next problem.

1.1 Playing the Factor Game

Mathematical Goals

- Become familiar with the factors of the numbers from 2 to 30
- Review multiplication and division of small whole numbers
- Begin to recognize the difference between prime numbers and composite numbers
- Relate dividing and finding factors of a number

Launch

Remind students that there are two ways to think of a factor: as one of the numbers that is multiplied to get a product, and as a divisor of a number.

- *What factors can you multiply to get a product of 10?*
- *What numbers divide 10 evenly?*
- *How are these two lists related?*

Introduce the Factor Game by playing a game against the class using the game board on Transparency 1.1. Explain the rules as the need arises during the game. Take the first turn choosing 26 for your first move, so students can later experience the power of a prime first move when they play the game with a partner.

Have students play the game two or three times with a partner.

Materials
- Transparencies 1.1A–1.1C
- Transparency markers

Vocabulary
- (whole number) factor
- (whole number) divisor
- proper factor

Explore

- *As you play the game, think about these questions.*

Write these questions on the board or overhead:

Is it better to go first or second? Why?

What is the best first move? Why?

How do you know when the game is over?

How do you know when you have found all the factors of a number?

Going Further

- *Is there a way to have all the numbers circled on the game board?*
- *What is the fewest number of factors that can be circled in a finished game?*
- *What is the worst first move? Is that the only possibility?*

Materials
- Labsheet 1.1
- Calculators (optional)

Summarize

Have a few students share some ideas they discovered while playing the game.

Discuss the four questions above as a whole class.

Include students' first descriptions of factors and divisors in the vocabulary section of their notebooks.

Summarize information using Summary Transparency 1.1D.

Materials
- Summary Transparency 1.1D
- Student notebooks

ACE Assignment Guide for Problem 1.1

Core 1–7
Other *Connections* 28–31, *Extensions* 39

Adapted For suggestions about adapting ACE exercises, see the CMP *Special Needs Handbook.*

Answers to Problem 1.1

A. Answers will vary. A student may notice that 1 is the worst first move because you lose your turn, or that 29 is the best first move because it yields the highest point advantage.

B. You test the number by dividing it into the original number. If there is a whole number answer, then the number is a factor of the original number.

C. You divide the known factor into the original number. The quotient is another factor of the number.

D. Answers will vary. Possible answer: 24 has 1, 2, 3, 4, 6, 8, 12, and 24 as factors, while 7 only has 1 and 7 as factors.

E. The *factors* of 18 are 1, 2, 3, 6, 9, and 18. The *divisors* of 18 are 1, 2, 3, 6, 9, and 18. They are the same since in each case the word means that you can find a whole number that you can multiply by the factor or divisor and get the number 18.

F. When there are no numbers left that are less than the original number and that divide evenly into the original number. Some students may notice that it is enough to test only the numbers that are less than half the original number.

1.2 Playing to Win the Factor Game

Goals

- Classify numbers as prime or composite
- Recognize that some numbers are rich in factors, while others have few factors
- Review multiplication facts

This section helps students to recognize that some numbers are rich in factors, while others have few factors, and introduces the definitions of prime numbers and composite numbers. Other special numbers such as perfect, deficient, and abundant are also introduced in the summary, but they are not essential. This problem engages students in systematically analyzing the Factor Game. As they were playing the game, certain strategies may have occurred to them. Now they are encouraged to verbalize—and possibly explain—their insights.

Mathematics Background

For background on classifications of numbers, see page 4.

Launch 1.2

Suggested Questions The questions you wrote on the board in the Explore section of the last problem help to launch this problem.

- *Thinking about the best first move in the Factor Game makes me wonder what the results would be for each number if I chose it as my first move. What if I chose 1 or 2 or 3? How many points would I get? How many points would my opponent get?*

- *Let's find the results for every possible first move. Can you think of a way that we can organize our work so that we can see patterns and determine which moves are good and which moves are bad?*

Give your students a chance to suggest ways to approach the analysis and organization of their work. If no productive ideas surface, have them consider a tabular organization. If you want to provide your students with a chart for recording, use Labsheet 1.2.

Begin filling in the chart for a couple of first moves. Then, give students 5 to 10 minutes to work on their charts individually. Next, have them work with a partner to compare, correct, and complete their charts. Have students write the answers for Problem 1.2 in their notebooks.

You may want to make and display a class chart so you and your students can refer to it during the rest of the unit.

Explore 1.2

Suggested Questions As you are circulating, ask students questions about how they are finding the factors. Help them see that being systematic helps you not to miss any factors.

- *What strategy/strategies can you use to make sure you have found all the factors without missing any?*

- *How do you know when you have found all the factors of a number?*

- *If 6 is a factor of a number, what other factors will that number have?* (1, 2, 3)

For example, use the number 24. For the number 24, systematically testing the numbers beginning with 1 will be sure to get all factors.

- *Is 1 a factor?*
  (Yes. $1 \times 24 = 24$. So now 24 is also a factor.)

- *Is 2 a factor?*
  (Yes. $2 \times 12 = 24$. So 12 is also a factor.)

- *Is 3 a factor?*
  (Yes. $3 \times 8 = 24$. So 8 is also a factor.)

- *Is 4 a factor?*
  (Yes. $4 \times 6 = 24$. So 6 is also a factor.)

- *Is 5 a factor?* (5 is not a factor.)

- *Is 6 a factor?* (Yes, $6 \times 4 = 24$, but we have already listed this one! Some students may need to test every number up to 24 to be convinced that nothing else can work except those we have already found.)

Summarize 1.2

Students should record the results of the discussion in their notebooks, either in class or as a part of their homework.

Suggested Questions These questions can be used to discuss the problem and introduce prime and composite numbers, and abundant, deficient, and perfect numbers. (As the class discusses these questions, you can use different colored markers to circle the different numbers on the class chart of first moves as they occur in the discussion.)

- *What is the best first move?* (29, because you get 29 points and the other person gets 1 point.)

- *Are there any other first moves where your opponent would only get 1 point?* (yes)

- *What are they?* (2, 3, 5, 7, 11, 13, 17, 19, and 23.)

As students name them, circle them on the classroom chart while students circle them on their charts.

- *How many factors do these numbers have?* (2)

- *We call these numbers* prime numbers. *A number is considered a good first move if the player picking the number scores more points than his or her opponent. Are all the prime numbers good first moves?* (Yes.)

- *What are the first moves that would allow your opponent to get more than one point?* (4, 6, 8, 9, 10, 12, 14, 15, 16, 18, 20, 21, 22, 24, 25, 26, 27, 28, 30)

As students name them, circle them in a different color on the classroom chart while students circle them on their charts.

- *How many factors do these numbers have?* (More than two, or students may begin listing them.)

- *We call these numbers* composite numbers. *Are composite numbers good first moves?* (Some like 27, 25, and 22 are okay. But others like 30 and 24 are terrible.)

- *Why wouldn't you want to choose 30 as a first move?* (Because your opponent gets more points than you do.)

- *Are there any other numbers where this happens?* (12, 18, 20, 24)

- *The sum of the proper factors of these numbers (12, 18, 20, 24, 30) is greater than the number. The ancient mathematicians called these numbers* abundant numbers.

- *When the sum of the proper factors of a number is equal to the number, the ancient mathematicians called these* perfect numbers. *Are there any perfect numbers in our list?* (6, 28)

- *Are there any first moves that make you lose a turn?* (1) *Why?* (It does not have any proper factors.) *Because 1 does not have any proper factors, it is neither prime nor composite.*

Introduce vocabulary words as students describe situations in the game. (For instance, when students discuss moves in which their opponent gets more points than they do, introduce *abundant numbers*.)

Summary Transparency 1.2

A useful way to check for understanding is to use the questions on Summary Transparency 1.2.

1. *How do you know when you have found all the factors of a number?* (Students may say, "You have checked all the numbers up to the number itself," or they may have developed some other strategies.)

2. *How many proper factors does 1 have?* (None.)

3. *Would a prime number be a good second move?* (No, because you would lose a turn. All proper factors would have been circled.)

4. *Teri said, "All the prime numbers are odd." Would you agree?* (No. 2 is a prime number and it is even.)

5. *What is the next prime number after 29?* (31)

6. *Are there any first moves where your opponent would get the same score as you?* (Some numbers, 6 and 28, would give your opponent the same score as you.)

7. *Rosie said, "Every other first move has 2 as a factor." Would this pattern continue? Why or why not?* (Yes, because odds and evens alternate, and every even number is divisible by 2.)

8. *Why does every number (except 1) have 1 as a proper factor?* (Because every number is divisible by 1.)

Another question you may pose:

9. *Suppose we had a factor board with the numbers 1 to 49. What would be the best first move? Why?* (47, because it is the greatest prime number that is less than 49.)

1.2 Playing to Win the Factor Game

Mathematical Goals

- Classify numbers as prime or composite
- Recognize that some numbers are rich in factors, while others have few factors
- Review multiplication facts

Launch

- *What if I choose 1 or 2 or 3 as a first move? Would any of those be good first moves? How many points would I get? My opponent?*
- *Let's find the results for every possible first move.*

After filling in the chart for a few first moves, give students 5–10 minutes to work on their charts individually. Next, have them work with a partner to compare, correct, and complete their charts. When their charts are complete, have them write the answers for Problem 1.2 in their notebooks.

Explore

Circulate. Ask students questions about how they are finding the factors.

- *What strategy can you use to make sure you have found all the factors?*
- *How do you know when you have found all the factors of a number?*

Materials
- Labsheet 1.2
- Large chart like Labsheet 1.2 for display in classroom

Summarize

As a class, discuss answers to Problem 1.2 by asking the questions below.

- *What is the best first move?*
- *Are there any other first moves where your opponent would only get 1 point? What are they?*

Circle them on the classroom chart while students circle them on their charts.

- *How many factors do these numbers have? We call these* prime numbers. *Are all the prime numbers good first moves?*
- *What first moves allow your opponent to get more than one point?*

Circle them in a different color on the charts.

- *How many factors do these numbers have? We call these numbers* composite numbers. *Are composite numbers good first moves?*
- *Why wouldn't you want to choose 30 as a first move? Are there any other numbers where this happens? The sum of the proper factors of these numbers (12, 18, 20, 24, 30) is greater than the numbers themselves. The ancient mathematicians called these numbers* abundant numbers.
- *When the sum of the proper factors of a number is equal to the number, these are called* perfect numbers. *Are there any perfect numbers in our list?*
- *Are there any first moves that you make you lose a turn? Why?*

Check for understanding using Summary Transparency 1.2.

Materials
- Summary Transparency 1.2
- Student notebooks

Vocabulary
- prime number
- composite number

Optional Vocabulary
- abundant number
- perfect number
- deficient number

ACE Assignment Guide for Problem 1.2

Core 8, 10–13, 15, 16
Other *Applications* 9, 14; *Connections* 32–34; *Extensions* 40–44; unassigned choices from previous problems

Adapted For suggestions about adapting ACE exercises, see the CMP *Special Needs Handbook*.

Answers to Problem 1.2

A. 1–2.

First Move	Proper Factors	My Score	Opponent's Score
1	None	0	0
2	1	2	1
3	1	3	1
4	1, 2	4	3
5	1	5	1
6	1, 2, 3	6	6
7	1	7	1
8	1, 2, 4	8	7
9	1, 3	9	4
10	1, 2, 5	10	8
11	1	11	1
12	1, 2, 3, 4, 6	12	16
13	1	13	1
14	1, 2, 7	14	10
15	1, 3, 5	15	9
16	1, 2, 4, 8	16	15
17	1	17	1
18	1, 2, 3, 6, 9	18	21
19	1	19	1
20	1, 2, 4, 5, 10	20	22
21	1, 3, 7	21	11
22	1, 2, 11	22	14
23	1	23	1
24	1, 2, 3, 4, 6, 8, 12	24	36
25	1, 5	25	6
26	1, 2, 13	26	16
27	1, 3, 9	27	13
28	1, 2, 4, 7, 14	28	28
29	1	29	1
30	1, 2, 3, 5, 6, 10, 15	30	42

3. Possible answers: 1 is a factor of all numbers; 1 is the worst first move because you lose a turn; some numbers have only two factors, 1 and that number itself; all of the numbers with two factors are odd except 2; the numbers 4, 9, 16, and 25 have an odd number of factors and are even, odd, even, odd, so the next number with an odd number of factors will be even.

B. 29; it gives you the greatest point advantage over your opponent.

C. 1; if you choose 1, you lose your turn because 1 has no proper factors for your opponent to choose.

D. 24 and 30; your opponent gets 12 points more than you get. (Students may not understand that 24 and 30 are equally bad first moves. The fact that it is the difference between the scores of you and your opponent that matters is a difficult concept to grasp.)

E. 2, 3, 5, 7, 11, 13, 17, 19, 23, and 29

F. Prime numbers are good first moves. A prime number has only two factors: the number itself and 1. Since the only proper factor of a prime number is 1, your opponent scores only 1 point. Large prime numbers are the best moves. For example, 29 gives you 29 points and your opponent only 1 point. However, you should choose a prime number only as the first move. If you chose a prime for any other move, you would lose your turn and not score, because the only proper factor, 1, would have already been circled.

G. 4, 6, 8, 9, 10, 12, 14, 15, 16, 18, 20, 21, 22, 24, 25, 26, 27, 28, and 30

H. A composite number with many proper factors would be a bad first move, because your opponent would get many points. Composite numbers with proper-factor sums that are greater than the number are the worst first moves. For example, if you choose 30 or 24 as a first move, your opponent will score 12 points more than you will. Not all composite numbers are bad first moves. For example, if you choose 25, you will get 25 points and your opponent will only get 6.

1.3 Playing the Product Game

Goals

- Develop understanding of factors and multiples and the relationships between them
- Understand that some products are the result of more than one factor pair (for example, $18 = 9 \times 2$ and $18 = 6 \times 3$)
- Review multiplication facts

This section reviews multiplication facts, develops understanding of the relationship between factors and multiples, and helps students recognize that some products have more than one factor pair. The Factor Game required students to find factors of numbers. In the Product Game, students explore multiples and deepen their understanding of factors.

Launch 1.3

Suggested Question Before you introduce the game, make sure your students understand what a product is.

- *We are going to learn to play a new game called the Product Game. What does the word* product *mean?*

When you are satisfied students can give examples of products with understanding, introduce the Product Game.

The best way to explain the rules is to play a game against the class. Use Transparency 1.3 on the overhead projector, or draw a game board on the chalkboard.

Explain that the numbers at the bottom of the board are the only factors that can be used in the game.

Suggested Question You might ask students:

- *The game is played on a grid of numbers. Look at the numbers in the grid. Why are these numbers included?* (The numbers in the grid are the products that can be made by multiplying any two of the given factors.)

As you play the game, use two colors to mark the products, one to mark the class's products and the other to mark your own.

A typical game might begin like this:

1. Place a paper clip on 4 in the factor list. Explain to the class that you do not get to mark a product in the grid, because it takes two factors to make a product.

2. Ask the class to select a factor. Suppose they pick 7. Place a paper clip on 7. Ask the class to compute the product of 4 and 7. Mark the result, 28, on the game board using the class's color. Note: There is no need to keep score, because the goal of the game is to place four markers in a row—up and down, across, or diagonally.

3. Remove the paper clip from 7 and place it on the 4 in the factor list. Explain to the class that since the factors are both 4, the product is 16. Use your color to mark 16 on the product grid.

4. Continue playing until you or your class get four in a row.

Have students pair up to play the game. You may wish to laminate game boards for repeated use.

Explore 1.3

- *As you play the game, think about whether it is better to go first or second. Make notes about the strategies that will help you win the game.*

After students have played the game two or three times, have them work on the questions in the problem. These questions will prepare them for the class summary.

Be on the lookout for students who have not sorted out *factor*, *product*, and *multiple* and their relationships.

Summarize 1.3

Have a class discussion about whether it is better to go first or second. Have students share any strategies they discovered while playing the game.

Here are some comments students have made:

It is better to go second, because if you go first, you do not get to make a move on the board.

When you get toward the end of the game, you have to avoid the factors of the numbers your opponent needs.

If you have to go first, you should choose the number 1 because it gives your opponent fewer choices about where to go to get four in a row.

These observations may not come up, but you could pose them for students to comment on.

Go over all of the questions in the problem. This is especially important, since the word *multiple* is introduced for the first time. You can also use a number sentence to make sure students understand the vocabulary.

- *I am going to write a number sentence on the board. I want you to use the words* factor, divisor, multiple, product, divisible by, *and any other new words from this investigation to write as many statements as you can about the sentence.*

Write on the overhead or board: $5 \times 6 = 30$. Some possible sentences are:

30 is a multiple of 5 and of 6.

5 is a factor of 30.

6 is a divisor of 30.

30 is divisible by 5.

30 is divisible by 6.

The product of 5 and 6 is 30.

5 is a prime number because it has only 1 and 5 as factors.

6 is a composite number because it has 1, 2, 3, and 6 as factors.

Suggested Questions At this point it might be useful to ask some questions that compare factors and multiples.

- *Is there a number that is both a factor and a multiple of 15? Why or why not?* (15 is a factor and a multiple of itself.)

- *In the Factor Game, suppose you start a turn. What number could you select that would result in the number 12 being circled?* (If one student chooses the number 24, the other student could circle 12.)

- *In the Product Game, describe a play that would result in the number 12 being circled.* (12 could be circled if 3 and 4 were chosen as factors, or if 2 and 6 were chosen as factors.)

Summary Transparency 1.3C

You can use the questions on Summary Transparency 1.3C to probe deeper into students' understanding.

1. *What do you think is a good strategy for playing the Product Game?* (A good strategy for playing the product game is to try to go second—but if you go first, to choose the number 1 because it gives your opponent fewer choices about where to go to get four in a row. You have to avoid the factors of the numbers your opponent needs.)

Here are Jing's and Paul's strategies:

Jing If I want to cover a certain number on the grid, I check to see if one of the paper clips is on a factor of that number. If it is, I know I can move the other paper clip to get the product I want.

Paul I try to mark a row, column, or diagonal with numbers that have a lot of factors. That way, there will be a better chance I will be able to get the products that I want.

2. *Do you think their strategies are good ones?* (Yes, their strategies are good ones.)

3. *Is there a good first move in this game?* (A good first move is the number 1, just as Shinghi suggests.)

Shinghi If I have to go first, I put my paper clip on 1. This way my opponent can only get a number at the top of the board.

4. *Does her strategy offer any advantages?* (When you start with the number 1, your opponent has fewer choices about where to get four in a row.)

Check for Understanding

ACE Exercise 45 or 46 can serve as a quick assessment.

Some students may enjoy making up a Factor Game with a different set of factors or a different size board. This can be done as homework. If you do suggest this, you may want to set some conditions on the size of the board.

Comparing the Factor and Product Games

Before discussing the Reflection questions, you should ask the class to compare the factor and product games. Some of the things that should surface are:

> In the factor game, you start with a number and find all its factors. So this number is the multiple of each of the numbers that are factors. This number is also the product of two of the factors. Some numbers have more than one factor pair.

> In the product game, you start with factors and find the product of two factors. The product is also a multiple of each of the factors.

Multiples are discussed in more detail later in the unit, but some students will come in with some understanding of multiples.

The concepts of factor and multiple are interdependent. If A is a factor of B, then B is a multiple of A. This means that we can find a number C such that the product of A and C equals B; that is, $A \times C = B$. From this we see that factors always come in pairs. For example, we know that $3 \times 4 = 12$. This says that 3 is a factor of 12 and that 4 is a factor of 12. The two are a factor pair because their product is equal to 12. Also 12 is the product of 3 and 4. It is also a multiple of each number. In fact, there are several statements that can describe the relationships in the number fact $3 \times 4 = 12$. We can say the following:

> 3 is a **factor** of 12. Or 12 is a **multiple** of 3.

> 4 is a **factor** of 12.

> 3 is a **divisor** of 12.

> 4 is a **divisor** of 12.

> 12 is the **product** of 3 and 4. Or 12 is a **multiple** of 3 and of 4.

> 12 is a **multiple** of 3.

> 12 is a **multiple** of 4.

> 12 is **divisible by** 3.

> 12 is **divisible by** 4.

1.3 The Product Game

PACING $1\frac{1}{2}$ days

Mathematical Goals

- Develop understanding of factors and multiples and the relationships between them
- Understand that some products are the result of more than one factor pair (for example, $18 = 9 \times 2$ and $18 = 6 \times 3$)
- Review multiplication facts

Launch

Make sure students understand what a product is.

- *We are going to learn to play a new game called the Product Game. What does the word* product *mean?*

Play a game against the class. Explain the rules as you play.

Explain that the numbers at the bottom of the board are the only factors that can be used in the game. You might ask students:

- *The game is played on a grid of numbers. Look at the numbers in the grid. Why are these numbers included?*

Have students play the game two or three times in pairs.

Materials

- Transparencies 1.3A and 1.3B
- 2 paper clips
- Transparency markers

Explore

- *As you play the game, think about whether it is better to go first or second. Make notes about the strategies that will help you win the game.*

Then have them work on the questions in the problem.

Watch for students who have not sorted out *factor*, *product*, and *multiple* and their relationships.

Materials

- Labsheet 1.3
- Paper clips
- Colored chips or markers (2 different colors)

Summarize

Have students share any strategies they discovered while playing the game. Discuss all of the questions in the problem.

- *Is it better to go first or second? Is there a best first move?*
- *Is it possible to get every product with the given factors?*
- *Are any products missing for these factors?*
- *If you want to circle 12, how could you do it?*
- *What are multiples of 5 in the game board? Not on the board?*

Use a number sentence to make sure students understand the vocabulary. Write on the overhead or board: $5 \times 6 = 30$.

- *I want you to use the words* factor, divisor, multiple, product, divisible by, *and any other new words from this investigation to write as many statements as you can about the sentence.*

Materials

- Summary Transparency 1.3C
- Student notebooks

Vocabulary

- multiple

Optional Vocabulary

- divisible by
- near-perfect number
- square number

continued on next page

Summarize
continued

Use Summary Transparency 1.3C to continue the strategy discussion. Ask some questions that compare factors and multiples.

- *Is there a number that is both a factor and a multiple of 15? Why or why not?*
- *In the Factor Game, describe a play that would result in the number 12 being circled.*
- *In the Product Game, describe a play that would result in the number 12 being circled.*

Check for Understanding

Use ACE Exercise 45 or 46 as a quick assessment.

ACE Assignment Guide for Problem 1.3

Core 17, 19–21, 23, 24, 27, 35–37
Other *Applications* 18, 22, 25, 26; *Connections* 38, *Extensions* 45–49; unassigned choices from previous problems

Adapted For suggestions about adapting Exercise 18 and other ACE exercises, see the CMP *Special Needs Handbook*.

Answers to Problem 1.3

A. Answers will vary. Students may notice that selecting squares near the center gives more options for adding adjacent squares. They may also notice that there are multiple ways to get some cells, but only one way to get others. For example, the products of 2 and 6 and of 3 and

4 are both 12. However, 7 is the product of only 1 and 7.

B. Yes. You can see this by checking each number in the grid.

C. No. Every possible product appears in the grid. You can see this by listing every possible product and checking to see that they are all on the game board or by systematically checking the multiples of each number in the factor list.

D. You can get 12 as the product of 2 and 6 or 3 and 4.

E. 1. $5 \times 1 = 5, 5 \times 2 = 10, 5 \times 3 = 15,$
   $5 \times 4 = 20, 5 \times 5 = 25, 5 \times 6 = 30,$
   $5 \times 7 = 35, 5 \times 8 = 40,$ and $5 \times 9 = 45$

   2. Answers will vary. Other multiples include 50, 60, 6,000,000, 5555, and 85.

The student edition pages for this
investigation begin on the next page.

Notes _____
_____
_____
_____

Investigation 1

Factors and Products

Jamie is 12 years old. Her cousin, Emilio, is 2 years old. Her brother, Cam, is 3. Her neighbor, Esther, is 8. The following number sentences say that Jamie is

6 times as old as Emilio,   4 times as old as Cam,   and $1\frac{1}{2}$ times as old as Esther.

$$12 = 6 \times 2 \qquad\qquad 12 = 4 \times 3 \qquad\qquad 12 = 1\frac{1}{2} \times 8$$

Notice that each of the whole numbers 2, 3, 4, and 6 can be multiplied by another whole number to get 12. For this reason, 2, 3, 4, and 6 are called *whole-number factors*, or *whole-number divisors*, of 12.

Although 8 *is* a whole number, it *is not* a whole-number factor of 12 because you cannot multiply 8 by another whole number to get 12.

To save time, we will simply use the words **factor** and **divisor** to refer to whole-number factors and whole-number divisors of a number.

6   Prime Time

Notes _____

_____

_____

_____

1.1 Playing the Factor Game

Playing the Factor Game is a fun way to practice finding factors of whole numbers. If you pay close attention, you may learn some interesting things about numbers that you didn't know before! To play the game, you need a Factor Game Board and colored pens, pencils, or markers.

active math
online

For: Factor Game Activity
Visit: PHSchool.com
Web Code: amd-1101

The Factor Game

1	2	3	4	5
6	7	8	9	10
11	12	13	14	15
16	17	18	19	20
21	22	23	24	25
26	27	28	29	30

Factor Game Rules

1. Player A chooses a number on the game board and circles it.

2. Using a different color, Player B circles all the proper factors of Player A's number. The **proper factors** of a number are all the factors of that number, except the number itself. For example, the proper factors of 12 are 1, 2, 3, 4, and 6. Although 12 is a factor of itself, it is not a proper factor.

3. Player B circles a new number, and Player A circles all the factors of the number that are not already circled.

4. The players take turns choosing numbers and circling factors.

5. If a player circles a number that has no factors left that have not been circled, then that player does not get the points for the number circled and loses the next turn.

6. The game ends when there are no numbers left with uncircled factors.

7. Each player adds the numbers that are circled with his or her color. The player with the greater total is the winner.

Investigation 1 Factors and Products   **7**

STUDENT PAGE

Notes _____

_____

_____

_____

(7) 30

The First Five Moves of a Sample Game

This table shows the first five moves of a game between Cathy and Keiko.
The first column describes the moves the players made. The other columns
show the game board and the score after each move.

Action	Game Board	Score

Cathy circles 24.
Keiko circles 1, 2, 3,
4, 6, 8, and 12 (the
proper factors of 24).

Cathy	Keiko
24	36

Keiko circles 28. Cathy
circles 7 and 14 (the
factors of 28 that are
not already circled).

Cathy	Keiko
24	36
21	28

Cathy circles 27.
Keiko circles 9 (the
only factor of 27 that
is not already circled).

Cathy	Keiko
24	36
21	28
27	9

Keiko circles 30.
Cathy circles 5,10 and
15 (the factors of 30
that are not already
circled).

Cathy	Keiko
24	36
21	28
27	9
30	30

Cathy circles 25.
All the factors of 25
are circled. Cathy does
not receive any points
for this turn and loses
her next turn.

Cathy	Keiko
24	36
21	28
27	9
30	30
0	0

8 Prime Time

Notes

Problem 1.1 Finding Proper Factors

A. Play the Factor Game several times with a partner. Take turns making the first move. Look for moves that will give you more points than your opponent. As you play, write down any strategies or patterns you find.

B. How can you test to determine whether a number is a factor of another number?

C. If you know a factor of a number, can you find another factor? Explain your thinking.

D. Give an example of a number that has many factors and an example of a number that has few factors.

E. Make a list of the factors of 18. Make a list of the divisors of 18. Are the factors of a number also divisors of the number? Explain your thinking.

F. How do you know when you have found all the factors of a number?

ACE **Homework starts on page 14.**

Playing to Win the Factor Game

Did you notice that some numbers are better than others to choose for the first move in the Factor Game? For example, if you choose 22, you get 22 points and your opponent gets only $1 + 2 + 11 = 14$ points. However, if you choose 18, you get 18 points, and your opponent gets $1 + 2 + 3 + 6 + 9 = 21$ points!

Now you will make a table to analyze the Factor Game and look for patterns. Your table might start like this:

First Move	Proper Factors	My Score	Opponent's Score
1	None	Lose a Turn	0
2	1	2	1
3	1	3	1
4	1, 2	4	3

Investigation 1 Factors and Products **9**

STUDENT PAGE

Notes _____

_____

_____

_____

Problem 1.2 Prime and Composite Numbers

A. 1. Make a table of all the possible first moves (numbers from 1 to 30) in the Factor Game.

2. For each move, list the proper factors of the number, and record the scores you and your opponent would receive.

3. Describe an interesting pattern you see in your table.

B. What is the best first move? Why?

C. Which first move would make you lose your next turn? Why?

D. Other than your answer to Question C, what is the worst first move? Why?

E. List all the first moves that allow your opponent to score only one point. These numbers are called *prime numbers*.

F. Are all prime numbers good first moves? Explain. (Remember, a number is a *good first move* if the player choosing the number scores more points than his or her opponent.)

G. List all the first moves that allow your opponent to score more than one point. These numbers also have a special name. They are called *composite numbers*.

H. Are composite numbers good first moves? Explain.

ACE Homework starts on page 14.

Did You Know?

Large prime numbers are used to encode top-secret information. In 1999, Nayan Hajratwala found a prime number with more than 2 million digits. In type this size, that number would be more than 2 miles long! The Electronic Frontier Foundation awarded Mr. Hajratwala $50,000 for discovering the first prime number with more than 1,000,000 digits. The EFF now offers a prize of $250,000 to the first person to find a prime number with over 1,000,000,000 digits!

Notes _____

_____

_____

_____

Mathematicians have always been puzzled about fast ways of determining whether really big numbers are prime. In August, 2002, Dr. Manindra Agrawal and two college students, Neeraj Kayal and Nitin Saxena, made a breakthrough. They surprised and delighted mathematicians with an elegant way of determining whether really huge numbers are prime. You can find more information about this in the August 8, 2002, issue of *The New York Times*.

Go Online
PHSchool.com
For: Information about prime numbers
Web Code: ame-9031

1.3 The Product Game

You learned about factors of a number in Problems 1.1 and 1.2. In the next game you will learn about multiples of numbers. A **multiple** of a number is the product of that number and another whole number. For example, 24 is a multiple of 6 because $4 \times 6 = 24$. Multiples and factors have an interesting back-and-forth relationship.

If a number is a multiple of 5, then 5 is a factor of that number. These five sentences describe how the numbers 3, 5, and 15 are related.

$$5 \times 3 = 15$$

5 is a factor of 15.

3 is a factor of 15.

15 is a multiple of 5.

15 is a multiple of 3.

You can probably think of other ways to show the relationship. For example, you could add these to the list:

15 is divisible by 5.

15 is divisible by 3.

Investigation 1 Factors and Products   **11**

Notes _____

_____

_____

_____

In the Factor Game, you start with a number and find its factors. In the Product Game, you start with factors and find their product. The Product Game board consists of a list of factors and a grid of products. The object is to mark four products in a row—up and down, across, or diagonally—before your opponent does.

For: Product Game Activity
Visit: PHSchool.com
Web Code: amd-1103

The Product Game

1	2	3	4	5	6
7	8	9	10	12	14
15	16	18	20	21	24
25	27	28	30	32	35
36	40	42	45	48	49
54	56	63	64	72	81

Factors:

1 2 3 4 5 6 7 8 9

To play the game, you need a Product Game Board, two paper clips, and colored markers or chips—one color for each player.

Product Game Rules

1. Player A puts a paper clip on a number in the factor list. Player A does not mark a square on the product grid because only one factor has been marked. It takes two factors to make a product.

2. Player B puts the other paper clip on any number in the factor list (including the same number marked by Player A). Player B then shades or covers the product of the two factors on the product grid. An example is shown on the next page.

3. Player A moves *either* paper clip to another number, leaving one in its original place, and then shades or covers the new product.

4. Each player, in turn, moves a paper clip and marks a product. If a product is already marked, the player does not get a mark for that turn. The winner is the first player to mark four squares in a row—up and down, across, or diagonally.

Notes _____

_____

_____

_____

Problem 1.3 Finding Multiples

A. Play the Product Game several times with a partner. Look for interesting patterns and strategies that might help you win. Make notes on your observations.

B. Examine the Product Game Board. Is it possible to get every number on the product grid by multiplying two of the numbers in the factor list? Justify your answer.

C. Can you find two numbers in the list of factors for the game whose product is *not* on the product grid?

D. Suppose that a game is in progress and you want to cover the number 12 on the grid. Describe one way this can happen. Can you get 12 in more than one way?

E. 1. Suppose that a game is in progress and one of the paper clips is on 5. What products can you make by moving the other paper clip?

     2. List five multiples of 5 that are not on the game board.

ACE Homework starts on page 14.

The Product Game

1	2	3	4	5	6
7	8	9	10	12	14
15	16	18	20	21	24
25	27	28	30	32	35
36	40	42	45	48	49
54	56	63	64	72	81

Factors:
1 2 3 4 5 6 7 8 9

How can I get 12?

Investigation 1 Factors and Products **13**

Notes _____

_____

_____

_____

Applications

1. Ben claims that 12 is a factor of 24. How can you check to determine whether he is correct?

2. What factor is paired with 6 to give 24?

3. What factor is paired with 5 to give 45?

4. What factor is paired with 3 to give 24?

5. What factor is paired with 6 to give 54?

6. How would you test to see whether 7 is a factor of 291?

7. **Multiple Choice** Which of these numbers has the most factors?

   A. 6   **B.** 17   **C.** 25   **D.** 36

8. Lareina understands factors, but sometimes she has trouble finding all the factors of a number. What advice would you give to help her find all the factors of a number? Demonstrate by finding all the factors of 110.

9. Find two numbers that have 2, 3, and 5 as factors. What other factors do the two numbers have in common?

10. **a.** What do you get when you use your calculator to divide 84 by 14? What does this tell you about 14 and 84?

    b. What do you get when you use your calculator to divide 84 by 15? What does this tell you about 15 and 84?

11. Ramona says the Factor Game might also be called the Divisor Game. Do you agree? Why or why not?

STUDENT PAGE

Notes _____

_____

_____

_____

12. a. Is 6 a divisor of 18? Why or why not?

 b. Is 18 a divisor of 6? Why or why not?

13. Which of these numbers are divisors of 64?

 2   6   8   12   16

14. In Exercise 13, Evan noticed that some of the proper factors of 64 can be multiplied to get another proper factor of 64. For example, 2 and 8 are factors of 64, and 16 is also a factor of 64. Does every number have some factors for which this is true?

For: Help with Exercise 14
Web Code: ame-1114

15. a. A prime number has exactly two factors, 1 and itself. If you circle a prime number in the Factor Game, your opponent will receive at most one point. Explain why. Give some examples.

 b. A composite number has more than two factors. If you circle a composite number in the Factor Game, your opponent might receive more points than you. Explain why. Give some examples.

16. Why is the set of factors of a number not the same as the set of proper factors of that number?

17. Using the terms *factor, divisor, multiple, product,* and *divisible by,* write as many statements as you can about the number sentence $4 \times 7 = 28$.

18. Dewayne and Todd are playing the Product Game. Dewayne's markers are on 16, 18, and 28, and Todd's markers are on 14, 21, and 30. The paper clips are on 5 and 6. It is Dewayne's turn to move a paper clip.

 a. List the moves Dewayne can make.

 b. Which move(s) would give Dewayne three markers in a row?

 c. Which move(s) would allow him to block Todd?

 d. Which move do you think Dewayne should make? Explain.

The Product Game

1	2	3	4	5	6
7	8	9	10	12	14
15	16	18	20	21	24
25	27	28	30	32	35
36	40	42	45	48	49
54	56	63	64	72	81

Factors:

1   2   3   4   5   6   7   8   9

Investigation 1 Factors and Products   **15**

Notes _____

_____

_____

_____

19. a. Suppose that one paper clip on the Product Game board is on 3. What products can you make by moving the other paper clip?

   b. List five multiples of 3 that are not on the game board.

   c. How many multiples of 3 are there?

20. Davis just marked 18 on the Product Game board. On which factors might the paper clips be placed? List all the possibilities.

21. Find two products on the Product Game board, other than 18, that can be made in more than one way. List all the pairs of factors that give each product.

22. Multiple Choice Which set represents all the factors of 12?

   F. {1, 2, 3, 4, 6, 12}   **G.** {12, 24, 36, 48, . . . }

   H. {0, 1, 2, 3, 4, 6, 12}   **J.** {1, 2, 3, 4, 6}

23. Use the ideas from this investigation to list at least five facts about the number 30.

24. Determine whether each of the following numbers can be made in more than one way in the Product Game. State whether the number is prime or composite.

   a. 36   **b.** 5   **c.** 7   **d.** 9

25. Salvador said that the Product Game might also be called the Multiple Game. Do you agree? Why or why not?

26. On the Product Game board, which number is both a prime number and an even number?

27. Jose says the Factor Game and the Product Game are similar because both involve multiplication. Marcus says they are not similar. With whom do you agree and why?

Connections

28. Twenty-five classes from Martin Luther King Elementary School will play the Factor Game at their math carnival. Each class has 32 students. How many game boards are needed if each pair of students is to play the game once?

Notes _____

_____

_____

_____

29. As part of the carnival, the school will hold a Factor Game marathon. It takes Archie and Kel an average of 12 minutes to finish one game. About how many games will they finish if they play nonstop from 9:00 A.M. to 2:30 P.M.?

30. Multiple Choice This week Carlos read a book for language arts class. He finished the book on Friday. On Monday he read 27 pages; on Tuesday he read 31 pages; and on Wednesday he read 28 pages. On Thursday and Friday he read the same number of pages each day. The book had 144 pages. How many pages did he read on Thursday?

A. 28 **B.** 29 **C.** 31 **D.** 58

31. Write a problem like Exercise 30 about a book you have read recently.

32. Long ago, people observed the sun's rising and setting over and over at about equal intervals. They decided to use the amount of time between two sunrises as the length of a day. They divided the day into 24 hours. Use what you know about factors to answer these questions:

a. Why is 24 a more convenient choice for the number of hours in a day than 23 or 25?

b. If you could select a number different from 24 to represent the number of hours in a day, what number would you choose? Why?

Notes _____

_____

_____

_____

33. a. In developing the ways in which we calculate time, astronomers divided an hour into 60 minutes. Why is 60 a good choice (better than 59 or 61)?

   b. If you could select another number to represent the number of minutes in an hour, what would be a good choice? Why?

34. a. Is 132 divisible by 12? By 3? By 4?

   b. Is 160 divisible by 10? By 2? By 5?

   c. Is 42 divisible by 6? By 3? By 2?

   d. What patterns do you see in parts (a), (b), and (c)?

For: Multiple-Choice Skills Practice
Web Code: ama-1154

For Exercises 35–37, find two numbers that can be multiplied to give each product. Do not use 1 as one of the numbers.

35. 84   **36.** 145   **37.** 300

38. a. Ms. Diaz wants to divide her class of 30 students into 10 groups, not necessarily of equal size. What are some of her choices?

   b. Ms. Diaz wants to divide her class of 30 students into equal-sized groups. What are her choices?

   c. How is the thinking you did in part (a) different from the thinking you did in part (b)?

Extensions

39. Jocelyn and Moesha decide to play the Factor Game on a 100-board, which includes the whole numbers from 1 to 100.

   a. What will Jocelyn's score be if Moesha chooses 100 as her first move?

   b. What will Jocelyn's score be if Moesha chooses 99 as her first move?

   c. What is the best first move on a 100-board?

40. What is my number?

   Clue 1 When you divide my number by 5, the remainder is 4.

   Clue 2 My number has two digits, and both digits are even.

   Clue 3 The sum of the digits is 10.

Notes _____

_____

_____

_____

41. The Factor Game can be played on a 49-board, which includes the whole numbers from 1 to 49.

    a. Use your table for analyzing first moves on a 30-board from Problem 1.2. Extend it to include all the numbers on a 49-board.

    b. What new primes do you find?

The Factor Game

1	2	3	4	5	6	7
8	9	10	11	12	13	14
15	16	17	18	19	20	21
22	23	24	25	26	27	28
29	30	31	32	33	34	35
36	37	38	39	40	41	42
43	44	45	46	47	48	49

42. Lana and Luis are playing the Factor Game on a 49-board. Lana has the first move and chooses 49.

    a. How many points does Luis score for this round?

    b. How many points does Lana score for this round?

43. What is the best first move on a 49-board? Why?

44. What is the worst first move on a 49-board? Why?

45. What three factors were used to make this Product Game board? What product is missing from the grid?

4	6	9
14	?	49

Factors: ___ ___ ___

46. What four factors were used to make this Product Game board? What product is missing from the grid?

9	15	18	
21	?	30	35
	36	42	49

Factors: ___ ___ ___ ___

Notes _____

_____

_____

_____

47. The sum of the proper factors of a number may be greater than, less than, or equal to the number. Ancient mathematicians used this idea to classify numbers as *abundant*, *deficient*, and *perfect*. Each whole number greater than 1 falls into one of these three categories.

  a. Draw and label three circles as shown below. The numbers 12, 15, and 6 have been placed in the appropriate circles. Use your factor table to determine what each label means. Then, write each whole number from 2 to 30 in the correct circle.

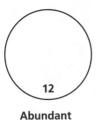
12
Abundant

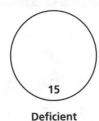
15
Deficient

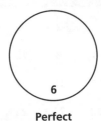
6
Perfect

  b. Do the labels seem appropriate? Why or why not?

  c. In which circle would 36 belong?

  d. In which circle would 55 belong?

48. Look at the Product Game board you used in Problem 1.3. Which of the numbers on that board can be formed by placing both paper clips on the same number? These numbers are called *square numbers*. Why do you think they have this name?

49. a. Suppose you choose 16 as a first move in the Factor Game. How many points does your opponent get? How does your opponent's score for this turn compare to yours?

  b. Suppose you choose 4 as a first move. How many points does your opponent get? How does your opponent's score for this turn compare to yours?

  c. Find some other numbers that have the same pattern of scoring as 4 and 16. These numbers could be called *near-perfect numbers*. Why do you think this name fits?

Did You Know?

Is there a largest perfect number? Mathematicians have been trying for hundreds of years to find the answer to this question. You might like to know that the next largest perfect number after 6 and 28 is 496.

Go Online
PHSchool.com
For: Information about perfect numbers
Web Code: ame-9031

STUDENT PAGE

Notes _____

_____

_____

Mathematical Reflections

In this investigation, you played and analyzed the Factor Game and the Product Game. These questions will help you summarize what you have learned.

Think about your answers to these questions. Discuss your ideas with other students and your teacher. Then write a summary of your findings in your notebook.

1. What are the factors of a number and how do you find them?

2. What did you learn about prime numbers and composite numbers while you were playing the Factor Game? Is the number 1 prime or composite? Explain.

3. What are the multiples of a number and how do you find them?

Unit Project What's Next?

Write something new that you have learned about your special number now that you have played the Factor Game and the Product Game.

Would your special number be a good first move in either game? Why or why not?

Notes _____

_____

_____

_____

Investigation ①

ACE Assignment Choices

Differentiated Instruction
Solutions for All Learners

Problem 1.1
Core 1–7
Other *Connections* 28–31, *Extensions* 39

Problem 1.2
Core 8, 10–13, 15, 16
Other *Applications* 9, 14; *Connections* 32–34; *Extensions* 40–44; unassigned choices from previous problems

Problem 1.3
Core 17, 19–21, 23, 24, 27, 35–37
Other *Applications* 18, 22, 25, 26; *Connections* 38; *Extensions* 45–49; unassigned choices from previous problems

Adapted For suggestions about adapting Exercise 18 and other ACE exercises, see the CMP *Special Needs Handbook*.

Applications

1. Divide 24 by 12 to see if you get a whole number. Since $12 \times 2 = 24$ or $24 \div 12 = 2$, 12 is a factor.

2. 4   3. 9   4. 8   5. 9

6. Divide 291 by 7 to see if the answer is a whole number. Since $291 \div 7 = 41.571428\ldots$, 7 is *not* a factor of 291.

7. D; 1, 2, 3, and 6 are the factors of 6; 1 and 17 are the factors of 17; 1, 5, and 25 are the factors of 25; 1, 2, 3, 4, 6, 9, 12, 18, and 36 are the factors of 36. So, 36 has the most factors.

8. Check every number beginning with 1 until you begin to get the same factors over again. With each small number factor you find, you will find a second factor when you divide.

   Factors of 110 are: 1, 2, 5, 10, 11, 22, 55, 110. I know I have found all of the factors because I checked all the numbers from 1 to 10, and then started getting repeats.

9. Answers will vary. 30 is the least possibility. Others are all multiples of 30. They may only have the numbers 1 and 30 as additional common factors. Common factors of any two such numbers must include 1, $2 \times 3 = 6$, $2 \times 5 = 10, 3 \times 5 = 15$ and $2 \times 3 \times 5 = 30$ in addition to 2, 3, and 5.

10. **a.** 6; Since the result is a whole number, 14 is a factor of 84.

    b. 5.6; Since the result is not a whole number, 15 is not a factor of 84.

11. I agree because a factor of a number is a divisor of the number.

12. **a.** Yes, $18 \div 6 = 3$.

    b. No, $6 \div 18 = 0.3333\ldots$.

13. 2, 8, 16

14. No. For example, 25 has only factors 1, 5, 25. There is no other factor relationship among the factors except the trivial cases of $1 \times 5 = 5$ and $1 \times 25 = 25$.

15. **a.** In the Factor Game, your opponent scores points for proper factors of the number you choose. The only proper factor of prime numbers, such as 2, 3, or 7, is 1.

    b. Some numbers, such as 12, 20, and 30, have many proper factors that would give your opponent more points. Some numbers, such as 9, 15, and 25, have fewer factors and would give you more points.

16. The proper factors do not include the number itself.

17. 4 is a factor of 28; 7 is a factor of 28; 4 is a divisor of 28; 7 is a divisor of 28; 28 is a multiple of 4; 28 is a multiple of 7; 28 is the product of 4 and 7; 28 is the product of 7 and 4; 28 is divisible by 4; 28 is divisible by 7.

18. **a.** Moving the paper clip from 6 to make the products $5 \times 1, 5 \times 2, 5 \times 3, 5 \times 4, 5 \times 5, 5 \times 7, 5 \times 8$, and 5×9; moving the paper clip from the 5 to make the products $6 \times 1, 6 \times 2, 6 \times 4, 6 \times 6, 6 \times 7, 6 \times 8$, and 6×9.

b. Moving the paper clip from 6 to 3, 4 or 9, makes 15, 20 or 45, respectively; moving the paper clip from the 5 to 7 makes 42.

c. Moving the paper clip from 5 to 7 makes 6×7, which is 42.

d. Possible answer: Moving the 5 to 7 to get 42; this blocks the opponent and gets 3 in a row.

19. **a.** $3 \times 1 = 3; 3 \times 2 = 6; 3 \times 3 = 9; 3 \times 4 = 12; 3 \times 5 = 15; 3 \times 6 = 18; 3 \times 7 = 21; 3 \times 8 = 24; 3 \times 9 = 27.$ So you can get a 3, 6, 9, 12, 15, 18, 21, 24, and 27, which are all multiples of 3.

b. $3 \times 11 = 33; 3 \times 13 = 39; 3 \times 17 = 51; 3 \times 19 = 57; 3 \times 20 = 60$ and many others.

c. There are infinitely many multiples of 3.

20. 2 and 9 or 3 and 6.

21. Answers should include two of the following:

16: 2×8 and 4×4 8: 1×8 and 2×4
12: 2×6 and 3×4 6: 1×6 and 2×3
4: 1×4 and 2×2

22. F; G contains the multiples of 12, H contains 0 which is not a factor of 12, and J contains the proper factors of 12.

23. Possible answer: the factors of 30 are 1, 2, 3, 5, 6, 10, 15, and 30; 30 is even; 30, 60, 90, . . . are multiples of 30; 30 is a composite number; 30 has 8 different factors.

24. **a.** 36 can be found on the product game by 6×6 or 4×9 and is composite.

b. 5 can be found on the product game by only 1×5 and is prime.

c. 7 can be found on the product game by only 1×7 and is prime.

d. 9 can be found on the product game by 1×9 or 3×3 and is composite.

25. Since the numbers on the game board are multiples of the numbers given as possible factors, you could argue in support of Sal's position.

26. 2

27. The two games are similar in that each focuses on the relationships found in a mathematical statement, such as: $3 \times 7 = 21$. This statement means the same thing as other members of its fact family: $21 \div 7 = 3$ and $21 \div 3 = 7$. The Product Game differs from the Factor Game in what the goal is. In the Factor Game you know the 21 and have to look for the 3 and 7 and all the other factors of 21. In the Product Game, you start with the 3 and 7 and find the 21. So you could argue for similar or not similar.

Connections

28. $25 \times 16 = 400$ boards

29. 5 hours $\times$ 60 minutes = 300 minutes; $300 + 30 = 330$ minutes. $330 \div 12 = 27.5$ so they can play 27 games.

30. B; $27 + 31 + 28 = 86; 144 - 86 = 58; 58 \div 2 = 29.$ Carlos read 29 pages on Thursday.

31. Answers will vary.

32. **a.** Since 24 has many factors, it can be divided into many equal parts. Since 23 is prime, it cannot be subdivided. The only proper factors of 25 are 1 and 5, so it can only be subdivided into 5 groups of 5.

b. Possible answers: 12, 18, 20, 28, 30, 32; these numbers have many factors.

33. **a.** Because 60 has many factors and 59 and 61 do not.

b. Possible answer: 100, since it has many factors.

34. **a.** Yes, $132 = 12 \times 11$, so it is divisible by 12. Yes, $132 = 3 \times 44$; yes, $132 = 4 \times 33$.

b. Yes, $160 = 10 \times 16$; yes, $160 = 2 \times 80$; yes, $160 = 5 \times 32$.

c. Yes, $42 = 6 \times 7$; yes, $42 = 3 \times 14$; yes, $42 = 2 \times 21$.

d. Answers will vary. Numbers that end in 2 or 0 are divisible by 2. If a number is divisible by a number, n, it is divisible by divisors or factors of n. Since 132 is divisible by 12, it must also be divisible by the factors of 12, including 3 and 4.

35. $12 \times 7, 42 \times 2, 4 \times 21, 6 \times 14,$ or 3×28

36. $5 \times 29 = 145$

37. $30 \times 10, 2 \times 150, 4 \times 75, 5 \times 60, 6 \times 50,$
$3 \times 100, 15 \times 20,$ or 12×25

38. a. Various answers: for example, group sizes $(1, 2, 4, 5, 6, 3, 2, 2, 3, 2)$. The goal is to find 10 numbers whose sum is 30.

b. Group sizes $(3, 3, 3, 3, 3, 3, 3, 3, 3, 3)$. If she does not have ten groups, she could have 1 group of 30 students, 2 groups of 15 students each, 5 groups of 6 students each, 6 groups of 5 students each, 10 groups of 3 students each, 15 groups of 2 students each, or 30 groups of 1 student each.

c. In part (a), the sum of the numbers in the ten groups must be 30. In part (b), we are considering *factors* of 30.

Extensions

39. a. $1 + 2 + 4 + 5 + 10 + 20 + 25 + 50$
$= 117$

b. $1 + 3 + 9 + 11 + 33 = 57$

c. 97

40. The numbers that have two even digits (Clue 2) and give a remainder of 4 when divided by 5 (Clue 1) are 24, 44, 64, and 84. Of these numbers, 64 is the only one with digits that add to 10 (Clue 3). The number is 64.

41. a.

First Move	Proper Factors	My Score	Opponent's Score
31	1	31	1
32	1, 2, 4, 8, 16	32	31
33	1, 3, 11	33	15
34	1, 2, 17	34	20
35	1, 5, 7	35	13
36	1, 2, 3, 4, 6, 9, 12, 18	36	55
37	1	37	1
38	1, 2, 19	38	22
39	1, 3, 13	39	17
40	1, 2, 4, 5, 8, 10, 20	40	50
41	1	41	1
42	1, 2, 3, 6, 7, 14, 21	42	54
43	1	43	1
44	1, 2, 4, 11, 22	44	40
45	1, 3, 5, 9, 15	45	33
46	1, 2, 23	46	26
47	1	47	1
48	1, 2, 3, 4, 6, 8, 12, 16, 24	48	76
49	1, 7	49	8

b. 31, 37, 41, 43, and 47

42. a. $1 + 7 = 8$　　**b.** 49

43. 47; it is the greatest prime number.

44. 48; the second player gets 76 points—28 more points than the first player.

45. 2, 3, and 7; 21 is missing

46. 3, 5, 6 and 7; 25 is missing

47. a.

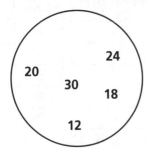

Abundant

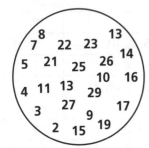

Deficient

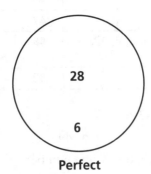

Perfect

b. *Abundant* means "more than enough," which is appropriate since the sum of an abundant number's proper factors is more than the number. *Deficient* means "not enough," which is appropriate since the sum of a deficient number's proper factors is less than the number. *Perfect* means "exactly right," which is appropriate because the sum of a perfect number's proper factors is equal to the number.

c. abundant   **d.** deficient

48. 1, 4, 9, 16, 25, 36, 49, 64, 81. If you use 4 dots to represent the number 4, you can make a 2 by 2 square of dots. 9 can be represented by a 3 by 3 square of dots, etc. . . . , so that may be one reason they are called square numbers.

49. a. $1 + 2 + 4 + 8 = 15$; your opponent scores one fewer point.

  b. $1 + 2 = 3$; your opponent scores one fewer point.

  c. 32, 64, 128, . . . , or any power of 2. The name *near-perfect* fits because the sum of the factors is 1 less than the total needed for the number to be perfect.

Possible Answers to Mathematical Reflections

1. A factor of a number is a number that divides the number with no remainder. (Another way to say this is that a number, a, is a factor of a number, b, if you can find another number, c, that makes a factor pair with a. This means that $a \times c = b$. The existence of the number, c, is the key.)

   You find factors of a number by testing each whole number, starting with 1. To test a number you divide it into the target number to see if it divides the target number with no remainder. If it is a divisor of the target number, the quotient is also a factor. You continue to test numbers until you begin to get repeats. Then you have them all.

2. Prime numbers have exactly two factors, themselves and 1.

   Composite numbers have more than two factors. The number 1 is neither prime nor composite. It has only 1 factor, so it satisfies neither criterion.

3. The multiples of a number, a, are all the numbers that the original number, a, divides evenly. The least multiple of a number, a, is $a \times 1$ which equals a. This means that every number is a multiple of itself. To find other multiples, you multiply the target number, a, by any whole number.

Investigation 2 — Whole-Number Patterns and Relationships

Mathematical and Problem-Solving Goals

- Recognize that factors come in pairs and that once one factor is found, another can also be found

- Visualize and represent a factor pair as the dimensions of a rectangle

- Determine whether a number is prime/composite, square/non-square, and even/odd based on its factor pairs

- Develop an informal sense of what factors must be checked to be sure all the factors of a number are found

- Make conjectures about the result of operations on odd numbers, on even numbers, and on combinations of odd and even numbers, and create arguments to show which conjectures are valid and which are not

- Determine whether a product is even or odd based on its factors

- Determine whether a sum is even or odd based on its addends

- Classify numbers by their characteristics using Venn diagrams as a tool for sorting and classifying

- Develop understanding of factors and multiples, common factors and common multiples, and the relationships among them

Summary of Problems

Problem 2.1 Finding Patterns

Students use square tiles to build all possible rectangles with a fixed number of tiles (fixed area). They explore the relationship between factors, factor pairs, and rectangles made to fit the factor pairs for a given number. This geometric interpretation of factor pairs adds to students' understanding of multiplication as well as the factors of a number.

Problem 2.2 Reasoning with Even and Odd Numbers

Students look at products and sums of even and odd numbers. The problem introduces students to the idea of making conjectures and providing arguments to "prove" or "disprove" those conjectures.

Problem 2.3 Classifying Numbers

Venn diagrams are used to introduce students to common multiples, common factors, least common multiples, and greatest common factors.

	Suggested Pacing	Materials for Students	Materials for Teachers	ACE Assignments
All	$3\frac{1}{2}$ days	Calculators; colored pens, pencils, or markers; blank transparencies and transparency markers (optional: for recording results); student notebooks	Blank transparencies and transparency markers	
2.1	1 day	Square tiles (about 30 per pair), grid paper (provided as a blackline master), blank sheets of paper, scissors, tape	Transparency 2.1	1–9, 22–24, 31–33
2.2	1 day		Transparency 2.2, models for odd and even numbers (optional)	10–16, 25, 34–35
2.3	1 day	Labsheets 2.3A and 2.3B (1 of each per pair)	Transparencies 2.3A–2.3C	17–21, 26–30, 36–41
MR	$\frac{1}{2}$ day			

Finding Patterns

Goals

- Recognize that factors come in pairs and that once one factor is found, another can also be found

- Visualize and represent a factor pair as the dimensions of a rectangle

- Determine whether a number is prime/composite, square/non-square, and even/odd based on its factor pairs

- Develop an informal sense of what factors must be checked to be sure all the factors of a number are found

Students make rectangles for each number from 1 to 30. Displaying the rectangles will help students to visualize a factor pair as the dimensions of a rectangle whose area is the given number. The displays will help students describe prime and square numbers.

They also explore the question of how you can predict when you will have found all the factors of a number. The rectangles students have created are used to focus students' thinking on how far you have to go to know that you have found all the factors. We can describe this idea as looking for the "turn around" point in finding factor pairs. This describes when the factors we are finding in pairs give no new factors.

Launch 2.1

Launch this problem by telling the story of the arts and crafts exhibit in the Getting Ready. Use the Getting Ready to help students understand the challenge that is coming in the problem. Let students work in pairs to find all the rectangles that can be made from 12 square yards. Use tiles to simulate the areas. Be sure that students know how to describe a rectangle by giving the dimensions of the rectangle. For example, a 3×4 rectangle has side lengths of 3 and 4. You can say that this rectangle is a 4×3 rectangle and picture it as a 3×4 rectangle rotated. Have some students cut out the different rectangles from grid paper or have a set ready to display.

Suggested Questions After they have all the rectangles, you might ask:

- *How is finding all the rectangles related to the work in Investigation 1?* (The dimensions of a rectangle with an area equaling 12 square yards form a factor pair for 12.)

- *What do all your rectangles for the number 12 have in common? What patterns do you see among the rectangles?*

Here are some observations students have made:

All the rectangles have 12 tiles.

All the rectangles can be turned and they look different.

Some rectangles repeat themselves.

The edge lengths are all factors of 12.

Arrange a display set of rectangles in order from the smallest base to the largest base. (Figure 1, next page)

Suggested Questions Point to the 2×6 rectangle.

- *How would you describe this rectangle?* (Help students connect factor pairs to the dimensions of a rectangle and the product to the number of tiles.)

- *What does this tell us about the numbers 2, 6, and 12?* ($2 \times 6 = 12$. 2 and 6 are factors of 12. Some might say that 12 is a multiple of 2 and of 6.)

- *When do the rectangles repeat themselves?* (They begin to repeat between 3 by 4 and 4 by 3.)

- *What does this say about the number of factors that you must check to make sure you have all the factors?* (If we check the numbers from 1 to 3 we have all the factors, because checking 1 also gives us the factor 12. Checking 2 also gives us the factor 6 and checking 3 gives us the factor 4.)

- *How can you use the factor pairs to find all the factors of 12?* (Look at the factors in the first three factor pairs. 1, 12, 2, 6, 3, 4)

Don't expect students to have complete understanding of these ideas. They will be explored in the problem and throughout this investigation.

Challenge the class to find all the rectangles for the numbers 1 to 30.

Divide the class into groups of 3 to 4, and assign a few numbers to each group. Make sure that each group has a prime number and some with many factors.

Give the directions for how they should record their work:

Each group makes a display that shows all the rectangles they found for each of their numbers. Put one number and its rectangles on one piece of paper. List the factors of the number from least to greatest on the bottom of the paper.

Explore 2.1

As groups finish, have them post their displays in order from 1 to 30.

When they have posted their numbers, make sure they work on Question B.

Suggested Questions When groups are ready, ask students to think about one or more of the following questions:

- *What patterns do you see in the rectangles you are making?*

- *What patterns do you see across all the numbers on which your group is working?*

- *What is the relationship between the rectangles for a number and the factors of the number?*

Figure 1

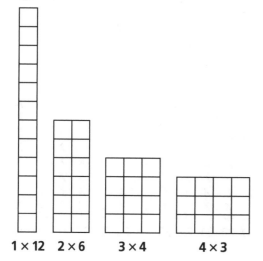

1×12 2×6 3×4 4×3 6×2 12×1

Going Further

Students who finish early and have correct work may wish to extend the display beyond 30. Some could work on 31, 32, or 36 as an extra challenge. Alternatively, you could extend the list to 50 or 60.

Summarize 2.1

Question A

Suggested Question Discuss with the class the patterns that students have found. Discuss the questions that you raised during the summary.

- *Look at the displays of rectangles for the numbers from 1 to 30. What patterns do you notice?* (Revisit the appropriate vocabulary as students describe the patterns.)

Here are some observations students have made:

Every number is something times 1.

Every even number has 2 as a factor.

1 has only one rectangle—a square—and only one factor. (1 is neither prime nor composite.)

24 and 30 have the greatest number of rectangles and, in the Factor Game, they were bad first moves. (24 and 30 are abundant numbers.)

All composite numbers have more than two rectangles because they have more than two factors, but primes have only two rectangles.

Half of every even number is a factor of that number.

Square numbers have an odd number of factors. This is because square numbers each have a number times itself as a rectangle, and this gives an odd number of factors.

If these observations do not come up, you can pose them as coming from a student in another class. Then ask them to comment on the patterns.

Suggested Questions Discuss with the class how to find the relationship between the dimensions of the rectangles and the factors of a number.

- *What is the relationship between the rectangles for a number and the factors of the number?* (The dimensions of the rectangles are all the factor pairs of a given number.)

- *Look at the factors at the bottom of the charts for the rectangles for the numbers 1 to 30. Compare the work in this problem to what you did in the last investigation.* (The lists of factors for the numbers 1 to 30 are the same as the list of factors that was generated in Problem 1.2, Playing to Win the Factor Game.)

Question B

Ask other questions that will help students make additional important observations. Here are examples of questions you might ask:

- *What numbers between 1 and 30 are prime?*

- *Which pairs of prime numbers differ by exactly 2? These are called* twin primes.

- *Which numbers have the most factors?*

- *Do greater numbers always have more factors than lesser numbers?*

- *How do you know how far you have to go in checking numbers to be sure you have found all the factors?*

- *Look at the number 12. Where do your rectangles turn around? (Call on several students and record their answers, for example, "between 4 × 3 and 3 × 4.")*

- *Can someone describe a pattern that might help determine the turn around point for a number such as 54?* (Student answers at this point will be informal:

Once the factor pairs repeat, I can stop checking for more factors.

The turn around point is the factor pair where the numbers are closest together.

You need to find the most squarelike rectangle.)

Check for Understanding

- *What are the factors of 32?*

- *How far must we check to find all the factors of 32?*

Repeat for 36 and 31.

One way to gauge students' understanding is to work with them to make a line plot and then look for patterns and groupings. The line plot below shows the numbers from 1 to 30 on the horizontal axis. The number of X's above each number indicates the number of factors the number has. (Figure 2)

Students could record groups of numbers with the same number of factors.

Suggested Questions

- *Which numbers have exactly two factors? What kind of numbers are these?* (Students should notice that all the prime numbers have exactly two factors.)

- *Which numbers have more than two factors? What kind of numbers are these?* (All the composite numbers have more than two factors.)

- *Which numbers have an odd number of factors? What kind of numbers are these?* (All the square numbers have an odd number of factors.)

Figure 2

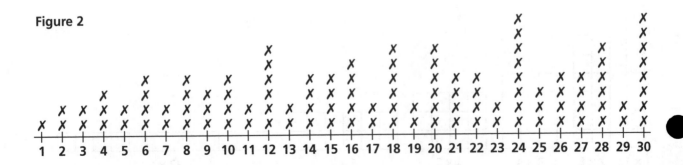

2.1 Finding Patterns

Mathematical Goals

- Recognize that factors come in pairs and that once one factor is found, another can also be found
- Visualize and represent a factor pair as the dimensions of a rectangle
- Determine whether a number is prime/composite, square/non-square, and even/odd based on its factor pairs
- Develop an informal sense of what factors must be checked to be sure all the factors of a number are found

Launch

Use the Getting Ready to make sure students understand the problem. Introduce the story. Have them use tiles and work with a partner to find all the rectangles made from 12 squares. Have students who finish quickly cut out models of the 6 rectangles as an example of what they will do in the problem. Line up the rectangles from the smallest base to the largest base.

- *What do you notice about all the rectangles?*
- *How would you describe this rectangle?* (Point to the 2×6 rectangle to get students to discuss the dimensions as factor pairs.)
- *What does that tell us about 2, 6, and 12?* (Review Investigation 1 ideas.)
- *What are all the factor pairs of 12?* (Record them.)
- *What are all the factors of 12 in order from least to greatest?* (Record.)
- *When do the factor pairs repeat? What does this tell us about how far we must check to make sure we have all the factors of a number?* (Let them think about this while they work on the problem.)

Pose the challenge of the problem. Have students work in small groups. Distribute a few numbers to each group.

Materials
- Transparency 2.1
- Square tiles

Vocabulary
- factor pair
- dimensions

Explore

- *What patterns do you see in the rectangles you are making?*
- *What is the relationship between the rectangles and the factors of a number?*

As groups finish, post displays in order from 1 to 30.

Going Further

- *If you are to find all the factors of a number, how far do you have to check to make sure you have all of them?*
- *How many factor pairs would 31, 32, or 36 have?*

Misconceptions

Listen for students who conjecture that the greater a number is, the more factors it has. During the summary, ask about this idea. Push them to find all the factors of 38 or 46 or 49.

Materials
- Grid paper (cm)
- Blank sheets of paper
- Scissors
- Tape

continued on next page

Ask the questions above and let the students discuss what patterns they found while making the rectangles.

- *Now that all our displays are on the wall for the numbers 1 to 30, what patterns do you notice?*

Revisit the appropriate vocabulary as students describe the patterns. If these ideas do not surface, ask:

- *Which numbers have the fewest rectangles? What kind of numbers are these?*
- *Which numbers are square numbers?*
- *Do greater numbers always have more factors than lesser numbers?*
- *How does this relate to previous work?*
- *How far do you have to go in checking numbers to be sure you have found all the factors?*
- *When will the factor pairs of a number begin to repeat?*
- *How far must we check to find all the factors of 32?*

Materials
- Student notebooks

Vocabulary
- square number

Optional Vocabulary
- even number
- odd number
- twin primes

ACE Assignment Guide for Problem 2.1

Core 1–9, 22–24; 31, 32
Other *Extensions* 33

Adapted For suggestions about adapting ACE exercises, see the CMP *Special Needs Handbook.*

Answers to Problem 2.1

A. Answers will vary.

B. 1. 24 and 30; possible answer: composite and abundant. (See Exercise 47 in Investigation 1.)

  2. 1 has only one rectangle, and 2, 3, 5, 7, 11, 13, 17, 19, 23, and 29 each have two. Possible answer: Except for 1, all these numbers are prime and deficient. (See Exercise 47 in Investigation 1.)

3. 1, 4, 9, 16, and 25

4. The dimensions of the rectangles are the factors of the number. For example, with 12 tiles, you can make rectangles with dimensions 1×12, 2×6, 3×4, 4×3, 6×2, and 12×1. The factors of 12 are the dimensions of these rectangles: 1, 2, 3, 4, 6, and 12.

2.2 Reasoning With Even and Odd Numbers

Goals

- Make conjectures about the result of operations on odd numbers, on even numbers, and on combinations of odd and even numbers, and create arguments to show which conjectures are valid and which are not

- Determine whether a product is even or odd based on its factors

- Determine whether a sum is even or odd based on its addends

Launch 2.2

Suggested Questions Review the concepts of odd and even numbers with your students.

- *In this problem, we will be working with odd and even numbers. What makes a number even, and what makes a number odd?*

Students may have many ideas. Be sure the definitions in the introduction to the problem in the Student Edition are discussed.

Go over the Getting Ready so that students have an idea of one way to model odd and even numbers.

- *Using the Getting Ready model, how are the models of even numbers different from the models of odd numbers?* (The models for even numbers are rectangles that are 2 squares tall; the models for odd numbers are not such rectangles. The odd-number models are rectangles with one extra square. The odd-number models could also be seen as rectangles that are missing a square.)

Then discuss what a conjecture is. Ask:

- *How do even and odd numbers differ from each other?*

- *What do you suppose happens when you add two of these numbers? Is the sum even or odd?* (Let students make some preliminary conjectures.)

- *In the problem, you are asked to make conjectures about the results of adding or multiplying odd and even numbers. A conjecture is your best guess about a relationship. For example, Question A of Problem 2.2 asks you to make a conjecture about whether the sum of two numbers is even or odd.*

- *After you have made a conjecture, try to show why it is true. Part of showing why something is true or false sometimes depends on finding a good way to model your ideas. Use tiles or anything else that makes sense to you to help figure out what happens when you add even and odd numbers in various combinations.*

Let students work in pairs.

Explore 2.2

As you circulate, look at the ways students are finding to model odd and even numbers. Be sure that the various strategies are discussed in the summary.

Going Further

For students who are ready for it, ask about combinations of sums or products of three or more odd or even numbers.

Summarize 2.2

Discuss the solutions, focusing not just on what happens, but on *why* it happens.

Some students may use the tile arrangement for whole numbers to make an argument:

The sum of two even numbers is even because you can just push the two rectangles, which each have 2 as a dimension, to make a new rectangle with 2 as a dimension. If 2 is a dimension, then the number has 2 has a factor and the number is even.

For example, if you add 6 and 4 you take the two rectangles 2 × 3 and 2 × 2 and put them together to make a 2 by 5 rectangle.

Odd numbers are made from an even number plus one. So when you add two odd numbers, you get the sum of two even numbers, which is even, and the sum of two ones, which is even.

$$5 = 4 + 1 \text{ and } 3 = 2 + 1$$
$$\text{So } 5 + 3 = 4 + 1 + 2 + 1$$
$$= 4 + 2 + 1 + 1$$
$$= 6 + 2$$
$$= 8$$

If you add two odd numbers, the extra tiles that stick out from each come together, resulting in a rectangle that has 2 as a dimension.

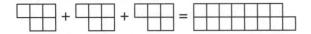

For multiplication, students may suggest putting rectangles together.

3×5 means taking three identical rectangles that have five tiles and stacking them together to make a rectangle with 15 tiles. Odd times Odd is odd.

2×5 means taking two identical rectangles that have five tiles and stacking them together to make a rectangle with 10 tiles. Even times Odd is Even.

Some students may use the structure of odd and even numbers:

When you multiply two odd numbers, the product has all the factors in the two numbers. Since 2 is not a factor of either number, it is not a factor of the product. For example, $3 \times 9 = 27$. The factors in 3 and 9 are 1, 3, and 9. In 27 the factors are 1, 3, 9 and 27. Since 2 is not a factor, the product is odd.

When you multiply an even and an odd number, the product will have a factor of 2 since the even number has a factor of 2. For example, $4 \times 9 = 36$. The factors of 4 and 9 are 1, 2, 4, 3, and 9. These, as well as 36 itself, are factors of 36. Since 2 is a factor, the product is even.

If your students seem ready, ask them to design a rule that will represent all the even whole numbers and another rule to represent all the odd whole numbers. Students may say that you just multiply the whole numbers by 2 to get the even numbers. If students say this, model what they are saying with a symbolic rule—2N where N is any whole number. So 2N represents even whole numbers and 2N + 1 represents odd whole numbers.

This discussion presents an opportunity to ask what you get if N is zero. This can lead to a discussion of Question B about whether zero is even or odd. It is even because it is divisible by 2.

For some students you will need to ask how you can inspect a number to decide whether it is odd or even. Get at what the digit in the ones place tells you.

Some students have a hard time making the leap from cases that can be modeled to the recognition that their conjectures are to work for all numbers—no matter how large. This means that we need to generalize the results. But students are still just at the very informal stage of their development of providing logical arguments or explanations.

Check for Understanding

- *Without doing the actual addition, are the following sums odd or even?*

    203 + 512   934 + 116   199 + 0

- *Without doing the actual multiplication, are the following products odd or even?*

    59×45 120×56 59×0

If students have trouble, ask:

- *Is each number odd or even? How can you tell?*

Mathematics Background

For background on formal proofs, see page 5.

2.2 Reasoning with Even and Odd Numbers

At a Glance

PACING 1 day

Mathematical Goals

- Make conjectures about the result of operations on odd numbers, on even numbers, and on combinations of odd and even numbers, and create arguments to show which conjectures are valid and which are not
- Determine whether a product is even or odd based on its factors
- Determine whether a sum is even or odd based on its addends

Launch

- *What did you notice about even numbers in our rectangular model displays of the factor pairs of a number?*
- *What makes a number even? What makes a number odd?*

Discuss the Getting Ready so students know what a conjecture is.

See if students can model odd and even numbers in some way.

- *What happens when you add two even numbers? Two odd numbers?*
- *You need to make a conjecture about each idea, and then find a way to convince everyone that your conjecture is true.*

Have students work in pairs.

Materials
- Models for odd and even numbers (optional)
- Transparency 2.2

Vocabulary
- even number
- odd number
- conjecture

Explore

Note ways students are finding to model the situation, so various strategies can be discussed in the summary.

Going Further

For those who are ready, ask about combinations for sums or products of three or more odd and even numbers.

Summarize

Discuss solutions; focus on what happens and why it happens.

If students are ready, push them to find a rule that will represent all even numbers and another rule to represent all odd numbers.

Materials
- Student notebooks

Check for Understanding

- *Without doing the actual addition, are the following sums odd or even?*

    203 + 512   934 + 116   199 + 0

- *Without doing the actual multiplication, are the following products odd or even?*

    59×45 120×56 59×0

continued on next page

Summarize
continued

Push for deeper understanding by asking:

- *How can you tell whether the sum of several numbers will be even or odd?*
- *How can you tell whether the product of several numbers will be even or odd?*

ACE Assignment Guide for Problem 2.2

Core 10–16, 25
Other *Extensions* 34–35; unassigned choices from previous problems

Adapted For suggestions about adapting Exercises 6–9 and other ACE exercises, see the CMP *Special Needs Handbook*.

Answers to Problem 2.2

A. 1. The sum of two even numbers is even. (Two rectangles with height 2 can be put together to form a larger rectangle with height 2.)

   2. The sum of two odd numbers is even. (The tile models for the odd numbers each have an extra square. If we combine the models, we can pair the extra squares to form a rectangle.)

   3. The sum of an odd number and an even number is odd. (One model for the even number is a rectangle with height 2. One model for the odd number is a rectangle with height 2 but with an extra square. If we combine the models, we still have an extra square.)

   4. The product of two even numbers is even. (If we put together an even number of even rectangles, we get another rectangle with no extra square.)

5. The product of two odd numbers is odd. (If we combine an odd number of rectangles with height 2 and an extra square, we get another rectangle with an extra square.)

6. The product of an even number and an odd number is even. (If we put together an odd number of even rectangles, we get another rectangle with no extra square.)

B. Zero is an even number. Students can argue that it has to be even because of the way odd and even numbers are distributed on the number line. They can also argue that 0 is divisible by 2, so it must be even. Finally, some students may point out that a "rectangle" of height 2, made with zero tiles, would have no extra tile.

C. You check to see whether each addend is odd or even and then use the conjectures that we have shown are true.

D. 1. 38, even; $3 + 5 \times 7 = 3 + 35 = 38$

   2. 19, odd; $25 - 3 \times 2 = 25 - 6 = 19$

   3. 82, even; $11 \times 5 + 3 \times 9 = 55 + 27 = 82$

   4. 40, even; $43 - 25 \div 5 + 2 = 43 - 5 + 2 = 38 + 2 = 40$

   5. 46, even; $43 - 7 + 5 \times 2 = 43 - 7 + 10 = 36 + 10 = 46$

   6. 20, even; $6 + 18 - 24 \div 6 = 6 + 18 - 4 = 24 - 4 = 20$

2.3 Classifying Numbers

Goals

- Classify numbers by their characteristics using Venn diagrams as a tool for sorting and classifying

- Develop understanding of factors and multiples, common factors and common multiples, and the relationships among them

A Venn diagram uses circles to show sets of numbers or other objects with the same attributes. Your students may have used string circles in the elementary grades to look at relationships or attributes. The important thing in this problem is for students to look for relationships and characteristics of numbers and to determine what numbers belong to a descriptor and what numbers fit more than one descriptor.

Launch 2.3

You might start the lesson by first having the students make a list of prime numbers less than 10 and another list of multiples of 2 less than 10. Then draw on the board or overhead two overlapping circles, labeled "Prime Numbers Less Than 10" and "Multiples of 2 Less Than 10."

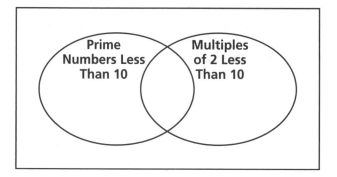

- *Now let's place all the numbers in each of your lists in the correct place in the circles.*

Record a few numbers that students give, always asking in which area of the diagram the number goes.

Suggested Questions

- *Are there any numbers that belong in both circles? Why or why not?*

Here we are hoping that students will see that there is a number that is prime and is a multiple of 2. They may need more help with this:

- *Is 2 a prime number? Why?*

- *Is 2 a multiple of 2? Why?*

- *We put the numbers that belong in both circles in the intersection, or overlap, of the circles. Therefore, 2 goes in the intersection.*

- *Is there another number that goes in this intersection?*

- *Are there any numbers that do not belong in either circle?*

Help students see that 1 and 9 are not primes and not multiples of 2, and therefore do not belong in either circle. Draw a rectangle that encloses the circles, and place these in the rectangle outside the circles.

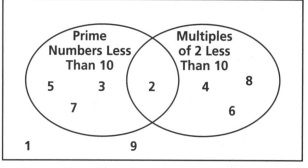

- *In the problem, you will have four different Venn diagrams to fill in. Look for the patterns that help you take short cuts and place several numbers quickly. Also, look for similarities and differences you notice in the four Venn diagrams.*

If you feel that there is not enough time to complete all four questions, assign at least two questions and give the rest to be completed outside of class. Be sure students understand that they will be expected to be ready for the summary when the class next meets. Make sure the students understand how the four diagrams are different from each other.

Let students work in pairs. When they are done, two pairs can share their work.

Explore 2.3

As you circulate, make sure that students are correctly placing numbers into the sections of the diagrams. If you spot trouble, ask students questions that will point to their errors. Ask about the placement of a number or two that would fall outside the circles.

Have students in each group describe what kinds of numbers belong in each of the sections of the Venn diagram.

Summarize 2.3

One way to summarize is to have each group draw their Venn diagrams on blank transparencies. The groups can then present their work at the overhead and explain their thinking. Alternatively, select four pairs of students, one for each problem, to put their work on the board.

Suggested Questions Be sure to ask questions such as the following:

- *What are the characteristics of the numbers that fall in the intersection of the two circles?*

- *As the circles overlap, they form three distinct parts. Describe what goes in each of the parts inside the circles but outside the intersection.*

- *What are the characteristics of the numbers that do not go inside the circles?*

- *What does it mean for a number to be a common factor of two numbers?*

- *What does it mean for a number to be a common multiple of two or more numbers?*

- *What is the least of the common multiples? How is it related to the other common multiples?*

- *How many common multiples can two numbers have?*

- *What is the greatest of the common factors? How is it related to the other common factors?*

Check for Understanding

You can also use the questions on Summary Transparency 2.3C to check for understanding.

Summary Transparency 2.3C

Luis and Maddie investigated Venn diagrams on their own. Here are some observations they made:

Luis *"In a Venn diagram showing the multiples of 5 and the multiples of 10, one circle can be completely inside the other."*

Maddie *"In a Venn diagram showing the factors of 45 and the factors of 32, the circles don't need to overlap at all because the numbers don't share any factors."*

1. *Do you agree with Luis' and Maddie's observations?* (Yes for Luis, but no for Maddie)

2. *Do you think it is possible to make a Venn diagram showing factors of two numbers, so that one circle is inside the other?* (yes)

3. *What would be the relationship between the numbers?* (The number in the inner circle would need to be a factor of the number in the outer circle.)

4. *Is it possible to make a Venn diagram showing the multiples of two numbers so that the circles don't overlap at all?* (No, since all numbers have a factor of 1.)

2.3 Classifying Numbers

Mathematical Goals

- Classify numbers by their characteristics using Venn diagrams as a tool for sorting and classifying
- Develop understanding of factors and multiples, common factors and common multiples, and the relationships among them

Launch

Make sure students understand how to use a Venn diagram. Draw two overlapping circles, label them "Prime Numbers Less Than 10" and "Multiples of 2 Less Than 10."

- *Give me some examples of numbers that go in each circle.*
- *Are there any numbers that belong in both circles? Why or why not?*
- *We put the numbers that belong in both circles in the intersection, or overlap, of the circles. Therefore, 2 goes in the intersection. Is there another number that goes in this intersection?*
- *Are there any numbers that do not belong in either circle?*

Draw a rectangle that encloses the circles, place 1 and 9 inside the rectangle but outside both circles.

- *In the problem, you will have four different Venn diagrams to fill in. Look for the patterns that help you take short cuts and place several numbers quickly. Also, look for similarities and differences you notice in the four Venn diagrams.*

Have students work in pairs.

Materials
- Transparencies 2.3A and 2.3B

Vocabulary
- Venn diagram

Optional Vocabulary
- intersection

Explore

Make sure students are correctly placing numbers into the diagrams.

- *Why does this number go here?*
- *What kind of numbers belong in each section of the diagram?*

Materials
- Labsheets 2.3A and 2.3B

Summarize

Have students display the results of the four diagrams and discuss the questions for each diagram. Summarize all the questions of the problem by asking:

- *What are the characteristics of the numbers that fall in the intersection of the two circles?*
- *What does it mean for a number to be a common factor of two numbers? What does it mean for a number to be a common multiple of two or more numbers? How many common multiples can two numbers have?*
- *What is the least of the common multiples? How is it related to the other common multiples? What is the greatest of the common factors? How is it related to the other common factors?*

Check for understanding of Venn diagrams with Summary Transparency 2.3C.

Materials
- Summary Transparency 2.3C
- Student notebooks

Optional Vocabulary
- greatest common factor
- least common multiple

Differentiated
Instruction
Solutions for All Learners

Core 17–21, 26–30
Other *Extensions* 36–41; unassigned choices from previous problems

Adapted For suggestions about adapting Exercise 19 and other ACE exercises, see the CMP *Special Needs Handbook*.

Answers to Problem 2.3

Note: Answers are given for all numbers through 50. This gives you some additional information.

A. Factors of 30: 1, 2, 3, 5, 6, 10, 15, and 30.
Factors of 36: 1, 2, 3, 4, 6, 9, 12, 18, and 36.

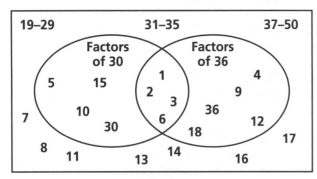

1. The numbers in the intersection are factors of both 30 and 36 (also factors of 6).

2. 7, 8, 11, 14, and 20 are possibilities. These are not factors of 30 or 36.

3. The numbers in the intersection are 1, 2, 3, and 6. The greatest of these is 6. So, 6 is the greatest common factor of 30 and 36.

4. 1 is the least common factor. 1 is a factor of all whole numbers, so it is in the intersection for diagrams for factors.

B. Factors of 20: 1, 2, 4, 5, 10, and 20.
Factors of 27: 1, 3, 9, and 27.

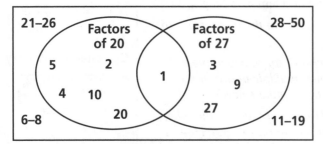

1. There is only one number in the intersection: 1. It is a factor of both 20 and 27.

2. The only number in the intersection is 1. It is the only common factor of 20 and 27. Since the only factor in common is 1, it is the greatest common factor.

3. In the diagram in Question A, there are several common factors. This diagram shows only 1 in the intersection since 20 and 27 have no common factors other than 1.

C. The multiples of 5 up to 40 are 5, 10, 15, 20, 25, 30, 35, and 40. The multiples of 4 up to 40 are 4, 8, 12, 16, 20, 24, 28, 32, 36, and 40.

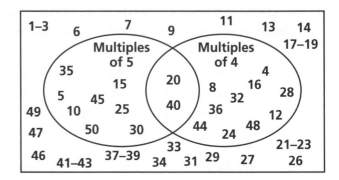

1. They are multiples of both 5 and 4.

2. The least number in the intersection is 20, so it is the least common multiple of 5 and 4.

3. 60, 80, 100, 120, 140, 160, etc. These numbers are all multiples of the least common multiple, which is 20. There is no *greatest* common multiple.

D. The multiples of 6 up to 48 are 6, 12, 18, 24, 30, 36, 42, and 48. The multiples of 8 up to 48 are 8, 16, 24, 32, 40, and 48.

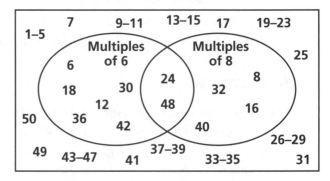

1. They are multiples of both 6 and of 8.

2. The least number in the intersection is 24. So, 24 is the least common multiple of 6 and 8.

3. In the Venn diagram for 5 and 4, only multiples of 5 × 4 are in the intersection. In the Venn diagram for 6 and 8, 24 is in the intersection, but it is not a multiple of 6 × 8.

The student edition pages for this
investigation begin on the next page.

Notes _____

_____

_____

_____

Investigation 2

Whole-Number Patterns and Relationships

Because you have been using whole numbers since you were young, you may think there is not much more to learn about them. However, there are many interesting relationships involving whole numbers that you may never have considered. To notice these relationships, it is sometimes helpful to break whole numbers into factors or to multiply them by other numbers.

2.1 Finding Patterns

In the Factor Game and the Product Game, you found that factors occur in pairs. Once you know one factor of a number, you can find another factor. For example, 3 is a factor of 12, and because $3 \times 4 = 12$, 4 is also a factor of 12. We call the pair 3, 4 a **factor pair.**

Every year, Meridian Shopping Mall has an exhibit of arts and crafts. People who want to display their work rent a space for $20 per square yard. Exhibitors are given carpet squares to lay out their spaces. Each carpet square measures 1 square yard. All exhibit spaces must have a rectangular shape.

22 Prime Time

Notes _____

_____

_____

_____

Terrapin Crafts wants to rent a space of 12 square yards. Use 12 square tiles to represent the carpet squares.

- What are all the possible ways the Terrapin Crafts owner can arrange the squares to make a rectangle?
- How are the rectangles you found and the factors of 12 related?

You just found all the possible rectangles that can be made from 12 tiles. These rectangles are *models* for the number 12. The models are useful because they allow you to "see" the factors of 12. You can make rectangle models such as these for any whole number.

In Problem 2.1, you and your classmates will use grid paper to create all the possible rectangle models for all the whole numbers from 1 to 30. When the rectangles are displayed, you can look for interesting patterns.

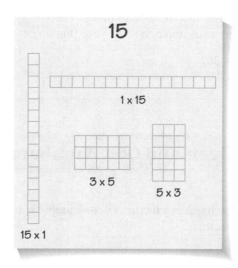

Your teacher will assign your group a few of the numbers from 1 to 30. Work with your group to decide how to distribute the numbers you have been assigned.

Investigation 2 Whole-Number Patterns and Relationships **23**

Notes

Problem 2.1 Rectangles and Factor Pairs

A. From grid paper, cut out all the possible rectangle models you can make for each of your numbers. You may want to use tiles to help you find the rectangles.

Write each number at the top of a sheet of paper, and tape all the rectangles for that number to the sheet. List the factors of the number from least to greatest at the bottom of the paper.

Display the sheets of rectangles in order from 1 to 30 around the room. When all the numbers are displayed, look for patterns.

B. 1. Which numbers have the most rectangles? What kind of numbers are these?

2. Which numbers have the fewest rectangles? What kind of numbers are these?

3. Which numbers are **square numbers** (numbers whose tiles can be arranged to form a square)?

4. How can you use the rectangle models for a number to list the factors of the number? Use an example to show your thinking.

ACE Homework starts on page 30.

2.2 Reasoning With Even and Odd Numbers

An **even number** is a number that has 2 as a factor. An **odd number** is a number that does not have 2 as a factor.

Notes _____

_____

_____

_____

Tilo makes models for whole numbers by arranging square tiles in a special pattern. Here are Lilo's tile models for the numbers from 1 to 7.

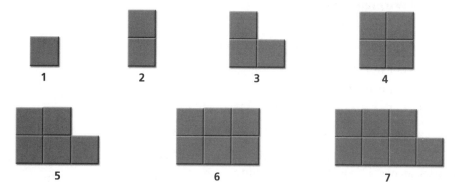

1   2   3   4

5   6   7

- How are the models of even numbers different from the models of odd numbers?

- Describe the models for 50 and 99.

When you tell what you think will happen in a mathematical situation, you are making a conjecture. A **conjecture** is your best guess about a pattern or a relationship that you observe. You can use models, drawings, or other kinds of evidence to support your conjectures.

Make a conjecture about what happens when you add two even numbers. Do you get an even number or an odd number? Why?

Problem 2.2 asks you to think of other conjectures to make about even and odd numbers.

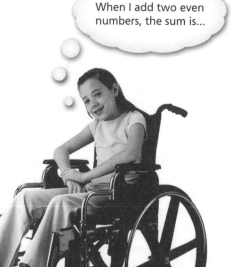

When I add two even numbers, the sum is...

Investigation 2 Whole-Number Patterns and Relationships   **25**

Notes

Problem **2.2** **Reasoning with Even and Odd Numbers**

A. Make conjectures about whether the results below will be even or odd. Then use tile models or some other method to support your conjectures.

  1. the sum of two even numbers

  2. the sum of two odd numbers

  3. the sum of an even number and an odd number

  4. the product of two even numbers

  5. the product of two odd numbers

  6. the product of an even number and an odd number

B. Is 0 an even number or an odd number? How do you know?

C. Without building a tile model, how can you determine whether a sum of numbers, such as $127 + 38$, is even or odd?

D. A problem occurs when we compute $6 + 3 \times 9$. You can get 81 or 33 as the answer! How can you get 81? How can you get 33? The *order of operations* rule says that you do all multiplications and divisions before you add or subtract. This makes 33 the correct answer.

Compute each number and tell whether it is even or odd.

  1. $3 + 5 \times 7$ **2.** $25 - 3 \times 2$ **3.** $11 \times 5 + 3 \times 9$

  4. $43 - 25 \div 5 + 2$ **5.** $43 - 7 + 5 \times 2$ **6.** $6 + 18 - 24 \div 6$

ACE **Homework starts on page 30.**

2.3 Classifying Numbers

A **Venn diagram** uses circles to group things that belong together. You can use Venn diagrams to explore relationships among whole numbers. For example, suppose that you want to group the whole numbers from 1 to 9 according to whether they are prime or multiples of 2. First, list the numbers that fall into each category:

  Prime Numbers: 2, 3, 5, 7   Multiples of 2: 2, 4, 6, 8

Next, draw and label two overlapping circles, one that represents the prime numbers and one that represents the multiples of 2. Put each number from 1 to 9 in the appropriate region. The numbers that don't fall into either category belong outside of the circles. The numbers that are in both categories belong in the overlap of the circles.

Notes _____

_____

_____

_____

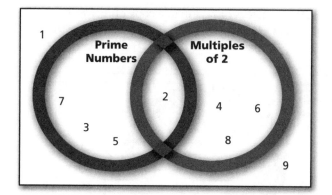

Problem 2.3 Classifying Numbers

The Venn diagrams in Questions A–D are related to the ideas you studied in Investigation 1.

A. List the factors of 30 and 36. Fill in a copy of this Venn diagram with all whole numbers less than or equal to 40. Then answer the questions below.

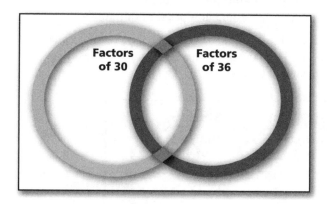

1. What do the numbers in the intersection (the "overlap") of the circular regions have in common?

2. List five numbers that fall in the region outside the circles and explain why they belong outside the circles.

3. Explain how you can use your completed diagram to find the greatest factor that 30 and 36 have in common. What is this *greatest common factor*?

4. What is the least number that falls in the intersection?

Notes

B. List the factors of 20 and the factors of 27. Fill in a copy of this Venn diagram with whole numbers less than or equal to 30. Then answer the questions below.

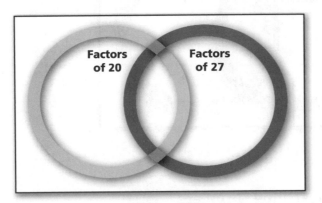

   1. What do the numbers in the intersection of the circular regions have in common?

   2. Explain how you can use your completed diagram to find the greatest factor that 20 and 27 have in common. What is this greatest common factor?

   3. Compare this Venn diagram to the one you completed in Question A. How are they alike, and how are they different?

C. List the multiples of 5 and the multiples of 4 that are less than or equal to 40. Fill in a copy of this Venn diagram with whole numbers less than or equal to 40. Then answer the questions that follow.

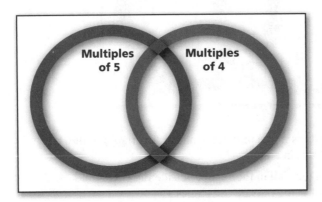

   1. What do the numbers in the intersection of the circular regions have in common?

Notes _____

_____

_____

_____

2. Explain how you can use your completed diagram to find the least multiple that 5 and 4 have in common. What is this *least common multiple*?

3. List five more numbers that would be in the intersection if numbers greater than 40 were allowed. What would be the greatest possible number in the intersection if you could use any number?

D. List the multiples of 6 and the multiples of 8 that are less than or equal to 48. Fill in a copy of this Venn diagram with whole numbers less than or equal to 48. Then answer the questions below.

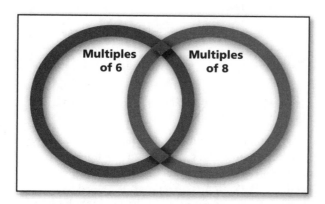

1. What do the numbers in the intersection have in common?

2. Explain how you can use your completed diagram to find the least multiple that 6 and 8 have in common. What is this least common multiple?

3. Compare this Venn diagram to the one you completed in Question C. How are they alike? How are they different?

ACE Homework starts on page 30.

Notes _____

_____

_____

_____

Applications

For Exercises 1–6, give the dimensions of each rectangle that can be made from the given number of tiles. Then use the dimensions of the rectangles to list all the factor pairs for each number.

1. 24 **2.** 32 **3.** 48 **4.** 45 **5.** 60 **6.** 72

7. What type of number has exactly two factors? Give examples.

8. What type of number has an odd number of factors? Give examples.

9. Luke has chosen a mystery number. His number is greater than 12 and less than 40, and it has exactly three factors. What might his number be? Use the display of rectangles for the numbers 1 to 30 from Problem 2.1 to help you find Luke's number. You may also need to think about what the displays for the numbers 31 to 40 would look like.

For Exercises 10–13, make a conjecture about whether each result will be odd or even. Use models, pictures, or other reasoning to support your conjectures.

10. An even number minus an even number

11. An odd number minus an odd number

12. An even number minus an odd number

13. An odd number minus an even number

Notes _____

_____

_____

_____

14. How can you tell whether a number is even or odd? Explain or illustrate your answer in at least two ways.

15. How can you determine whether a sum of several numbers, such as 13 + 45 + 24 + 17, is even or odd?

Homework
Help Online
PHSchool.com
For: Help with Exercise 15
Web Code: ame-1215

16. Insert operation signs to make the answer correct.

    a. 2 ■ 5 ■ 3 = 17   **b.** 2 ■ 5 ■ 3 = 13

    c. 2 ■ 5 ■ 3 = 30   **d.** 2 ■ 5 ■ 3 = 7

17. Copy this Venn diagram and place whole numbers from 1 to 36 in the appropriate regions. Do you notice anything unusual about the diagram?

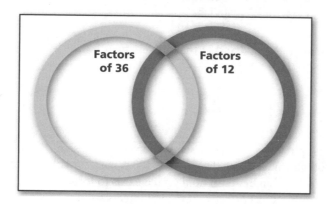

18. Copy this Venn diagram and find at least five numbers that belong in each region.

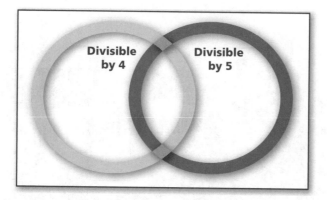

Notes _____

_____

_____

_____

19. a. Draw and label a Venn diagram in which one circle represents the multiples of 3 and another circle represents the multiples of 5. Place whole numbers from 1 to 45 in the regions of the diagram.

  b. List four numbers between 1 and 45 that fall in the region outside the circles.

  c. The *common multiples* of 3 and 5 (the numbers that are multiples of both 3 and 5) should be in the intersection of the circles. What is the least common multiple of 3 and 5?

20. a. Draw and label a Venn diagram in which one circle contains the divisors of 42 and another circle contains the divisors of 60.

  b. The *common factors* of 42 and 60 (the numbers that are divisors of both 42 and 60) should be in the intersection of the circles. What is the greatest common factor of 42 and 60?

21. Find all the common multiples of 4 and 11 that are less than 100.

Connections

22. The Olympic photograph below inspired a school pep club to design card displays for football games. Each display uses 100 square cards, At a game, groups of 100 volunteers will hold up the cards to form complete pictures. They are most effective if the volunteers sit in a rectangular arrangements. What rectangular seating arrangements are possible? Which arrangements would you choose? Why?

Notes _____

_____

_____

_____

23. A school band has 64 members. The band marches in the form of a rectangle. What rectangles can the band director make by arranging the members of the band? Which of these arrangements is most appealing to you? Why?

24. How many rectangles can you build with a prime number of square tiles?

25. Multiple Choice What is my number?

Clue 1 My number has two digits, and both digits are even.

Clue 2 The sum of my number's digits is 10.

Clue 3 My number has 4 as a factor.

Clue 4 The difference between the two digits of my number is 6.

A. 28   **B.** 46   **C.** 64   **D.** 72

26. a. List all the numbers less than or equal to 50 that are divisible by 5.

     b. Describe a pattern you see in your list that you can use to determine whether a large number—such as 1,276,549—is divisible by 5.

     c. Which numbers in your list are divisible by 2?

     d. Which numbers in your list are divisible by 10?

     e. How do the lists in parts (c) and (d) compare? Why does this result make sense?

27. Allie wants to earn some money for a new bike. She tells her dad she will wash the dishes for 2 cents on Monday, for 4 cents on Tuesday, and for 8 cents on Wednesday. If this pattern continued, how much would Allie earn on Thursday? How much would she earn altogether in 14 days?

28. Allie's eccentric aunt, May Belle, hides $10,000 in $20 bills under her mattress. If she spends one $20 bill every day, how many days will it take her to run out of bills?

29. a. What factor is paired with 6 to give 48?

     b. What factor is paired with 11 to give 121?

30. Using the terms *factor*, *divisor*, *multiple*, *product*, and *divisible by*, write as many statements as you can about the number sentence $6 \times 8 = 48$.

31. Multiple Choice Which number is a prime number?

F. 91   **G.** 51   **H.** 31   **J.** 21

Investigation 2 Whole-Number Patterns and Relationships   **33**

Notes _____

_____

_____

_____

32. Multiple Choice Which number is a composite number?

    A. 2   **B.** 79   **C.** 107   **D.** 237

Go Online
PHSchool.com

For: Multiple-Choice Skills Practice
Web Code: ama-1254

Extensions

33. Multiple Choice Which number is a square number?

    F. 128   **G.** 225   **H.** 360   **J.** 399

34. Find three numbers you can multiply to get 300.

35. a. Below is the complete list of the proper factors of a certain number. What is the number?

    1, 2, 3, 4, 6, 7, 12, 14, 21, 28, 42, 49, 84, 98, 147, 196, 294

    b. List each of the factor pairs for the number.

    c. How is the list of factor pairs related to the rectangles that could be made to show the number?

36. a. Find at least five numbers that belong in each region of the Venn diagram below.

    b. What do the numbers in the intersection have in common?

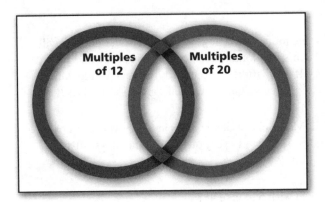

Consecutive numbers **are whole numbers in a row, such as 31, 32, 33, or 52, 53, 54. Think of different series of consecutive numbers when you work on Exercises 37–40.**

37. For any three consecutive numbers, what can you say about odd numbers and even numbers? Explain.

Notes _____

_____

_____

_____

38. Mirari conjectures that, in every three consecutive whole numbers, one number would be divisible by 3. Do you think Mirari is correct? Explain.

39. How many consecutive numbers do you need to guarantee that one of the numbers is divisible by 5?

40. How many consecutive numbers do you need to guarantee that one of the numbers is divisible by 6?

41. Jeff is trying to determine when to quit looking for more whole number factors of a number. He has collected data about several numbers. For example, 30 has 1×30, 2×15, 3×10, 5×6, and then he can stop looking, because the factor pairs repeat. For 36, he can stop looking when he gets to 6×6. For 66, there are no new factor pairs after 6×11. Copy and complete the table below. Is there any pattern that would help him know when to stop looking?

Number	16	30	36	40	50	64	66
Last Factor Pair	■	5×6	6×6	■	■	■	6×11

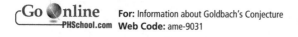

Many conjectures involving whole numbers seem simple, but are actually very difficult to justify. For example, in 1742, a mathematician named Christian Goldbach conjectured that any even number, except 2, could be written as the sum of two prime numbers. For example:

$$4 = 2 + 2 \qquad 12 = 7 + 5$$
$$36 = 17 + 19 \qquad 162 = 59 + 103$$

This seems like a pretty simple idea, doesn't it? However, in over 260 years, no one has been able to prove that it is true or find an even number that is not the sum of two prime numbers!

Go Online
PHSchool.com
For: Information about Goldbach's Conjecture
Web Code: ame-9031

Notes _____

_____

_____

_____

Mathematical Reflections 2

In this investigation, you classified numbers, analyzed factor pairs, and made conjectures about sums and products of odd and even numbers. These questions will help you summarize what you have learned.

Think about your answers to these questions. Discuss your ideas with other students and your teacher. Then write a summary of your findings in your notebook.

1. Think about the grid paper models in Problem 2.1. For any number, how can you use grid paper models to find the factor pairs for that number?

2. What are Venn diagrams? How are they useful for showing relationships among numbers?

3. What strategy do you use to find a complete list of factors for a given number? How do you know when you have found all the possible factors?

4. What do you know about the sums and products of odd and even numbers? Justify your statements.

Unit Project | What's Next?

Write about your special number. What can you say about your number now?

Is your number even? Is it odd?

How many factor pairs does your number have?

Notes _____

_____

_____

_____

Investigation 2

ACE Assignment Choices

Differentiated Instruction
Solutions for All Learners

Problem 2.1
Core 1–9, 22–24, 31, 32
Other *Extensions* 33

Problem 2.2
Core 10–16, 25
Other *Extensions* 34–35; unassigned choices from previous problems

Problem 2.3
Core 17–21, 26–30
Other *Extensions* 36–41; unassigned choices from previous problems

Adapted For suggestions about adapting Exercise 19 and other ACE exercises, see the CMP *Special Needs Handbook*.

Applications

1. dimensions: 1×24, 2×12, 3×8, 4×6, 6×4, 8×3, 12×2, 24×1
   factor pairs: 1, 24; 2, 12; 3, 8; 4, 6

2. dimensions: 1×32, 2×16, 4×8, 8×4, 16×2, 32×1
   factor pairs: 1, 32; 2, 16; 4, 8

3. dimensions: 1×48, 2×24, 3×16, 4×12, 6×8, 8×6, 12×4, 16×3, 24×2, 48×1
   factor pairs: 1, 48; 2, 24; 3, 16; 4, 12; 6, 8

4. dimensions: 1×45, 3×15, 5×9, 9×5, 15×3, 45×1
   factor pairs: 1, 45; 3, 15; 5, 9

5. dimensions: 1×60, 2×30, 3×20, 4×15, 5×12, 6×10, 10×6, 12×5, 15×4, 20×3, 30×2, 60×1
   factor pairs: 1, 60; 2, 30; 3, 20; 4, 15; 5, 12; 6, 10

6. dimensions: 1×72, 2×36, 3×24, 4×18, 6×12, 8×9, 9×8, 12×6, 18×4, 24×3, 36×2, 72×1
   factor pairs: 1, 72; 2, 36; 3, 24; 4, 18; 6, 12; 8, 9

7. Prime numbers have only two factors: 2, 3, 5, 7, 11, . . .

8. Square numbers have odd numbers of factors: 4, 9, 16, 25, 36, . . .

9. 25. His number must be a square number because it has an odd number of factors. 16 has five factors and 36 has nine factors.

10. An even number minus an even number is even. Students may use tiles for this, and they may show examples: $16 - 4$ is 12. Since an even number plus an even number is even, an even number minus an even number will still be even. They may give answers in terms of factors of two or in terms of "rectangles with height 2." For example, if you subtract one rectangle with height 2 from another rectangle with height 2, what you will have left will still be a rectangle with height 2.

    You can also see this by writing the equation
      EVEN + EVEN = EVEN
    and subtracting an even number from both sides. You are left with
      EVEN = EVEN − EVEN.

11–13. A student might illustrate this in terms of "rectangles with height 2" and "extra squares."

11. An odd number minus an odd number is even. If you have a rectangle with one extra square and you subtract a rectangle with one extra square, you have "subtracted the extra square" and are left with a rectangle with height 2.

12. An even number minus an odd number is odd. If you have a rectangle and you subtract a rectangle with one extra square, you have broken up a pair of squares and are left with another rectangle with an extra square.

13. An odd number minus an even number is odd. If you have a rectangle with one extra square and you subtract a rectangle, you still have an extra square and are left with a rectangle with an extra square.

14. Evens end in 0, 2, 4, 6, or 8, and they are divisible by two. Odds end in 1, 3, 5, 7, or 9, and they are not divisible by 2.

15. If all the numbers are even or if there is an even number of odd numbers, it is even. Otherwise it is odd.

16. **a.** $2 + 5 \times 3 = 17$

   b. $2 \times 5 + 3 = 13$

   c. $2 \times 5 \times 3 = 30$

   d. $2 \times 5 - 3 = 7$

17. There is no number that is a factor of 12 that is not also a factor of 36.

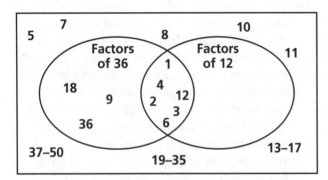

18. Answers may vary. Students should have five of the numbers shown in each region below.

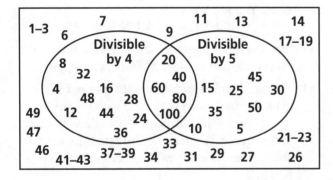

19. a.

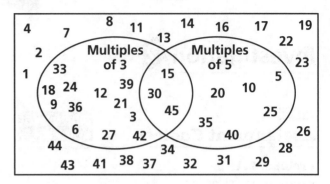

   b. Possible answers: 2, 4, 7, and 8

   c. 15

20. a.

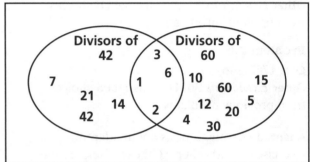

   b. 6

21. There are only two: 44 and 88.

22. 100 fans in 1 row, 50 fans in 2 rows, 25 fans in 4 rows, 20 fans in 5 rows, 10 fans in 10 rows, 5 fans in 20 rows, 4 fans in 25 rows, 2 fans in 50 rows, or 1 fan in 100 rows; Answers will vary, for example: I would rather have one long banner that wraps around part of the stadium, so I would choose 100 fans in one row. Or: I would rather have a big square that you could see on TV, so I would choose ten fans in ten rows.

23. 1×64, 2×32, 4×16, 8×8, 16×4, 32×2, and 64×1. Answers will vary as they did in Exercise 22.

24. 2   **25.** A

26. **a.** 5, 10, 15, 20, 25, 30, 35, 40, 45, 50

   b. All of these numbers end in 5 or 0.

   c. Those that end in 0.

   d. Those divisible by 2 and 5. They end in 0.

   e. They are the same—all numbers divisible by 10 are also divisible by 5 and 2.

27. On Thursday, she will earn 16 cents. In 14 days she will earn a total of $2 + 4 + 8 + 16 + 32 + 64 + 128 + 256 + 512 + 1,024 + 2,048 + 4,096 + 8,192 + 16,384 = 32,766$ cents, or $327.66.

28. 500 days

29. a. $8; 6 \times 8 = 48$ **b.** $11; 11 \times 11 = 121$

30. Possible answers: 48 is a multiple of 6; 8 is a divisor of 48; 48 is divisible by 8.

31. H   **32.** D

Extensions

33. G

34. Possible answers: $3 \times 10 \times 10; 2 \times 3 \times 50$

35. a. $2 \times 294 = 588$

   b. 1, 588; 2, 294; 3, 196; 4, 147; 6, 98; 7, 84; 12, 49; 14, 42; 21, 28

   c. There are twice as many rectangles as factor pairs: $1 \times 588, 2 \times 294, 3 \times 196, 4 \times 147, 6 \times 98, 7 \times 84, 12 \times 49, 14 \times 42, 21 \times 28$, and the reverses $28 \times 21, 42 \times 14, 49 \times 12, 84 \times 7, 98 \times 6, 147 \times 4, 196 \times 3, 294 \times 2$, and 588×1.

36. a. Possible answers: Multiples of 12 include 12, 24, 36, 48, and 72. Multiples of 12 AND 20 include 60, 120, 180, 240, and 300. Multiples of 20 include 20, 40, 80, 100, and 140. Multiples of neither include 1, 2, 3, 4, and 5.

   b. The multiples in the intersection are all divisible by 60.

37. Either two of the numbers are odd or two are even. If we start with an odd, we will have two odds, and if we start with an even, we will have two evens.

38. Since every third number on the number line is divisible by 3, any three consecutive whole numbers must include one that is divisible by 3.

39. 5   **40.** 6

41. (Figure 3) Students might notice that for square numbers the last factor pair, the turn around point, is the one that uses the square root, though they will not use that vocabulary word. Extending this idea to the non-square numbers, they may say that looking for a square near the number being investigated helps; thus, 66 is close to 8×8, and 7 and 8 are not factors of 66, so there is no point in looking further than 6×11.

Possible Answers to Mathematical Reflections

1. When you make rectangles on grid paper, the dimensions of those rectangles are the factor pairs of the number of squares enclosed. The number of rectangles you make is equal to the number of factors. For example, if you had 24 tiles, the dimensions of the rectangles are: $1 \times 24, 24 \times 1, 2 \times 12, 12 \times 2, 3 \times 8, 8 \times 3, 4 \times 6$, and 6×4. There are eight rectangles and eight factors of 24. The dimensions of these rectangles are the factor pairs of 24.

2. A Venn diagram uses circles to show sets of numbers or other objects. A number is inside a circle if it has a particular characteristic (such as being a factor of 30 or being a factor of 36). The overlap of the circles contains numbers that have both of these characteristics (such as being a factor of *both* 30 and 36). The area outside the circles contains numbers with none of these characteristics.

3. Look at the factor pairs that are the closest together, or the ones that form the most squarelike rectangle. You know that you have gone far enough when you check numbers up to this point, because it is the turn around point. After this, the factor that is paired with any greater factor will have already been tested.

Figure 3

Number	16	30	36	40	50	64	66
Last Factor Pair	4 × 4	5 × 6	6 × 6	5 × 8	5 × 10	8 × 8	6 × 11

4. The sum of two even numbers is even because you can combine two rectangles with height 2 to get another rectangle with height 2.

The sum of two odd numbers is even. The tile models for the odd numbers each have an extra square. If you combine the models, you can pair the extra squares to form a rectangle.

The sum of an odd number and an even number, or an even number and an odd number, is odd. If you combine the models, you still have an extra square.

The product of two even numbers is even. If you combine an even number of rectangles, you get another rectangle.

The product of two odd numbers is odd. If you combine an odd number of rectangles with an extra square, you get another rectangle with an extra square because you have an odd number of extra squares.

The product of an odd number and an even number, or an even number and an odd number, is even. If you put together an odd number of even rectangles, you get another rectangle. If you put together an even number of rectangles with extra squares, you get another rectangle.

Investigation Common Multiples and Common Factors

Mathematical and Problem-Solving Goals

- Recognize situations in which finding common multiples of whole numbers is important
- Develop strategies for finding common multiples
- Observe regularity or patterns in common multiples of numbers and use the patterns to reason about and predict future occurrences and solve problems
- Develop strategies for finding the least common multiple
- Begin to develop strategies for finding common factors
- Observe patterns in common factors of numbers and use the patterns to reason about and predict future occurrences and solve problems
- Recognize situations in which finding common factors of whole numbers is important
- Develop strategies for finding common factors and, in particular, the greatest common factor
- Recognize when common factors and greatest common factors are helpful in solving problems

Summary of Problems

Problem 3.1 Riding Ferris Wheels

This problem involves two siblings who get on two different-sized Ferris wheels at the same time. After what number of revolutions of the two wheels will the two siblings both arrive at the bottom? This is an application of common multiples. If we ask for the first revolution in which this happens, we are finding the least common multiple.

Problem 3.2 Looking at Cicada Cycles

This problem involves 13-year and 17-year cicadas, which struck a farm in 1935, and asks the question of when they might emerge together again. This problem explores common multiples and also deals with the least common multiple.

Problem 3.3 Bagging Snacks

Students investigate sharing snacks equally among a group. The problem leads to common factors and greatest common factors.

Problem 3.4 Planning a Picnic

Students determine the maximum number of people that can share a given number of drinks and snack crackers. This leads to the greatest common factor.

	Suggested Pacing	Materials for Students	Materials for Teachers	ACE Assignments
All	$4\frac{1}{2}$ days	Calculators, student notebooks	Blank transparencies and transparency markers	
3.1	1 day			1–8, 31, 32
3.2	1 day			9–15, 33–35, 37, 38
3.3	1 day			16–23, 39–41
3.4	1 day		Summary Transparency 3.4	24–30, 36, 42–44
MR	$\frac{1}{2}$ day			

Riding Ferris Wheels

Goals

- Recognize situations in which finding common multiples of whole numbers is important
- Develop strategies for finding common multiples
- Observe patterns in common multiples of numbers and use the patterns to reason about and predict future occurrences and solve problems

Launch 3.1

Suggested Questions

- *What are the first ten multiples of each number, 20 and 30?* (Notice that some students will not list the numbers themselves. This gives you an opportunity to emphasize that the least multiple of any number is the number itself.)

- *What numbers (multiples) occur on both lists? We call these* common multiples.

- *What do these numbers have in common?* (Each number is a multiple of 20 and of 30. Or, both 20 and 30 are factors of each number in the list.)

- *What is the least number that occurs on both lists?* (60) *This number is called the* least common multiple *of 20 and 30.*

Now ask questions about factors:

- *What are the factors of 12? Of 30?*

- *What numbers occur on both lists? We call these* common factors.

- *What properties do these numbers have in common?*

- *What is the greatest number on the list?* (6) *This number, 6, is called the* greatest common factor.

- *We are going to use the idea of common factors or common multiples to solve the problems in this investigation. How many of you have ever been on a Ferris wheel?*

- *Did you ever wonder about the number of trips around that you would get?*

- *What about the size of the Ferris wheel? How does it affect your ride?*

When you have the students wondering about these kinds of ideas, tell the class about the problem. A simple prop of two circles of different sizes can make the question clear.

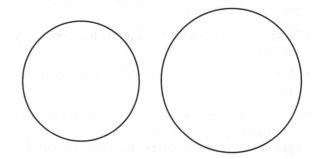

Mark a seat at the bottom point and put each circle on a screwdriver so that the two can be rotated simultaneously to model the Ferris wheels turning.

Give time for each student to think about the situations and to plan how they will try to solve them. Then let the class work in small groups of 2 to 4 to share ideas and solve the problem.

Explore 3.1

Remind the students to record their results in their notebooks.

Suggested Questions If some students are having difficulty, ask them questions to get them thinking.

- *After 20 seconds, where is the large Ferris wheel? The small Ferris wheel?* (The large wheel is only about a third of the way around. The small wheel has made one complete cycle and is back at the start.)

- *After 40 seconds, where is the large Ferris wheel? The small Ferris wheel?*

- *After 60 seconds, where is the large Ferris wheel? The small Ferris wheel?*

- *After 80 seconds, where is the large Ferris wheel? The small Ferris wheel?*

Have different groups put their answers to one of the parts on poster paper to use in the summary.

Going Further

If some groups have satisfactory answers, ask them to write two other problems about the time needed for the two Ferris wheels to both be at the bottom together again. The time for one problem should be the product of the times for each Ferris wheel. The time for the other problem should be less than the product of the times for each Ferris wheel.

Summarize 3.1

Suggested Questions Let the students share what answer they got as well as how they got it for each question. Then ask questions such as the following to see what students are noticing and to raise issues that they will continue to think about.

- *What are the common multiples for each set of numbers? Identify the least common multiple for each set.*

- *When is the least common multiple one of the numbers? What is special about these numbers that made that happen? Give another example for which this is true.*

- *When is the least common multiple the product of the two numbers? What is special about these numbers that made that happen? Give another example for which this is true.*

- *When is the least common multiple neither the product of the two numbers nor one of the numbers? What is special about these numbers that made that happen? Give another example for which this is true.*

- *As we work on the rest of this unit, try to notice other number pairs that produce these results.*

Students may not be ready to complete the answers to these questions, but by asking them now, students will have time to notice these patterns in other problems.

3.1 Riding Ferris Wheels

Mathematical Goals

- Recognize situations in which finding common multiples of whole numbers is important
- Develop strategies for finding common multiples
- Observe patterns in common multiples of numbers and use the patterns to reason about and predict future occurrences and solve problems

Launch

Review important vocabulary.

- *What are the first ten multiples of 20? Of 30?* (Make sure that students know that a number is a multiple of itself.)
- *What numbers (multiples) occur on both lists? We call these* common multiples.
- *What do these numbers have in common?*
- *What is the least number that occurs on both lists? This number is called the* least common multiple *of 20 and 30.*
- *What are the factors of 12? Of 30?*
- *What numbers occur on both lists? We call these* common factors.
- *What properties do these numbers have in common?*
- *What is the greatest number on the list? This number is called the* greatest common factor.

Discuss the context of Ferris wheels.

- *How many of you have ever been on a Ferris wheel?*
- *How many trips around do you get?*
- *How does the size of the wheel affect your ride?*

A simple prop of two circles of different sizes can make the question clear.

Have students work individually for a few minutes. Then go to pairs or small groups to share ideas and solve the problem.

Materials
- Student notebooks

Vocabulary
- common multiples
- least common multiple
- common factors
- greatest common factor

Explore

Remind the students to record their results in their notebooks.

For students having difficulty, ask questions to get them thinking:

- *After 20 seconds, where is the large Ferris wheel? The small one?*
- *After 40 seconds, where is the large Ferris wheel? The small one?*
- *Where are they after 60 seconds? After 80 seconds?*

Have groups put their answers on poster paper to use in the summary.

Materials
- Calculators

Going Further

See the extended section for details.

continued on next page

Summarize

Let students share their answers and explain how they got the answer to each question.

Have the class look at the common multiples for each set.

- *When is the least common multiple one of the numbers?*
- *When is the least common multiple the product of the two numbers?*
- *When is the least common multiple neither the product of the two numbers nor one of the numbers?*
- *What is special about the numbers that made each case happen?*
- *As we work on the rest of this unit, try to notice other number pairs that produce these results.*

Materials
- Student notebooks

ACE Assignment Guide for Problem 3.1

Core 1–5, 31, 32
Other *Applications* 6–8

Adapted For suggestions about adapting ACE exercises, see the CMP *Special Needs Handbook*.
Connecting to Prior Units 32: elementary school multiplication algorithms

Answers to Problem 3.1

A. Possible answer: You need to find the multiples of both 20 and 60. The multiples of 20 are 20, 40, 60, 80, 100, 120, 140, etc. The multiples of 60 are 60, 120, 180, 240, 300, 360, etc. The common multiples are 60, 120, 180, etc. The least common multiple is 60, so they would both be at the bottom after 60 seconds.

Take a little time to have students mentally compute the common multiple answers into minutes. For example: "The siblings will both be at the bottom every minute, with the big wheel going one revolution and the small one going around three times."

B. Possible answer: The multiples of 50 are 50, 100, 150, 200, 250, 300, 350, etc. The multiples of 30 are 30, 60, 90, 120, 150, 180, 210, 240, etc. The least common multiple is 150, so they would both be at the bottom after 150 seconds.

If needed, you could again ask the students to re-compute in minute language: "The siblings will both be at the bottom of the Ferris wheel every two and a half minutes (or 2 minutes, 30 seconds). The big wheel would have gone around three times and the small one five times."

C. Possible answer: The multiples of 10 are 10, 20, 30, 40, 50, 60, 70, 80, 90, 100, 110, etc. The multiples of 7 are 7, 14, 21, 28, 35, 42, 49, 56, 63, 70, 77, 84, 91, 98, 105, etc. The least common multiple is 70, so they would both be at the bottom after 70 seconds.

If needed, repeat the idea of conversion to minutes/seconds. You might also discuss with the students if it seems reasonable for a Ferris wheel to be able to make one revolution in 10 or 7 seconds.

D. Possible answers:

Question A: In 60 seconds, the large Ferris wheel makes 1 revolution, and the small Ferris wheel makes 3 revolutions.

Question B: In 150 seconds, the large Ferris wheel makes 3 revolutions, and the small Ferris wheel makes 5 revolutions.

Question C: In 70 seconds, the large Ferris wheel makes 7 revolutions, and the small Ferris wheel makes 10 revolutions.

Looking at Cicada Cycles

Goals

- Recognize situations in which finding common multiples of whole numbers is important

- Develop strategies for finding the least common multiple

- Observe patterns in common multiples of numbers and use the patterns to reason about and predict future occurrences and solve problems

Launch 3.2

Tell the class about 13-year and 17-year cicadas.

- *Here is another situation that considers when two or more things will happen again at the same time. Your challenge is to find when the two kinds of cicadas will appear again at the same time.*

Let the class work in small groups of 2–4.

Explore 3.2

Remind students to be ready to share their strategies as well as their solutions.

Suggested Question If the students are stuck, ask:

- *How is this problem similar to the one before and what strategies were used on that problem? How might we use those strategies here?*

Going Further

- *What do you need to find to answer questions like the Ferris wheel and the cicada problems?* (common multiples or least common multiples)

- *When is the LCM of two numbers one of the numbers? The product of the two numbers? Neither? What is special about the numbers that makes this happen?*

The summary is more inclusive and richer if students duplicate their responses onto an overhead transparency or chart paper for a visual presentation of their strategies and solutions.

Summarize 3.2

Have students talk about strategies and solutions. After the first pair/group of students has shared their strategy, ask if any other pair/group has a different strategy for solving that problem.

After the students have shared their solutions you might come back to the questions that you posed at the end of the summary for Problem 3.1:

- *How can we tell when the least common multiple will be the product of the two (or more) numbers given, and when the least common multiple will be less than the product of the two or more numbers given?*

Your students may not be able to answer these questions. Some students may get the answers, but for most students these generalizations are not necessary at this time.

Students can answer the problems by recognizing that common multiples are called for and then generate a list of common multiples. The least of these is the least common multiple.

Mathematics Background

For background on the least common multiple, see page 6.

3.2 Looking at Cicada Cycles

Mathematical Goals

- Recognize situations in which finding common multiples of whole numbers is important
- Develop strategies for finding the least common multiple
- Observe patterns in common multiples of numbers and use the patterns to reason about and predict future occurrences and solve problems

Launch

Tell the class about 13-year and 17-year cicadas.

- *Here is another situation that considers when two or more things will happen again at the same time. Your challenge is to find when the two types of cicadas will appear at the same time.*

Have students work in small groups.

Explore

Have students record their answers in their notebooks and in a way that can be displayed for class discussion.

For students having difficulty, ask questions to get them thinking:

- *How is this problem similar to what we've done before? What strategies were used on that problem? How can those strategies help here?*

Going Further

- *What do you need to find to answer questions like the Ferris wheel and cicada problems?*
- *When is the least common multiple of two numbers one of the numbers? The product of the two numbers? Neither? What is special about the numbers that makes this happen?*

Materials
- Calculators

Summarize

Have students talk about strategies and solutions. After the first pair/group of students have shared their strategy, ask if others have a different strategy for solving that problem.

After the students have shared their solutions you might come back to the questions posed at the end of the summary for Problem 3.1:

- *How can we tell when the least common multiple will be the product of the two (or more) numbers given, and when the least common multiple will be less than the product of the two or more numbers given?*

Some students may get the answers, but for most students these generalizations are not necessary at this time.

Materials
- Student notebooks

ACE Assignment Guide for Problem 3.2

Differentiated Instruction
Solutions for All Learners

Core 10, 11, 15
Other *Applications* 9, 12–14; *Connections* 33–35; *Extensions* 37, 38; unassigned choices from previous problems

Adapted For suggestions about adapting ACE exercises, see the CMP *Special Needs Handbook*.

Answers to Problem 3.2

A. Possible answers (using a listing method):

The multiples of 13 are 13, 26, 39, 52, 65, 78, 91, 104, 117, 130, 143, 156, 169, 182, 195, 208, 221, 234, ...

The multiples of 17 are 17, 34, 51, 68, 85, 102, 119, 136, 153, 170, 187, 204, 221, 238, ...

The least common multiple is 221. So it will be 221 years before these two cicada cycles will coincide again.

B. Possible answers (using a listing method):

The multiples of 12 are 12, 24, 36, 48, 60, 72, 84, 96, 108, 120, 132, 144, 156, 168, 180, 192, 204, 216, 228, 240, 252, 264, 276, 288, 300, 312, 324, 336, ...

The multiples of 14 are 14, 28, 42, 56, 70, 84, 98, 112, 126, 140, 154, 168, 182, 196 210, 224, 238, 252, 266, 280, 294, 308, 322, 336, ...

The multiples of 16 are 16, 32, 48, 64, 80, 96, 112, 128, 144, 160, 176, 192, 208, 224, 240, 256, 272, 288, 304, 320, 336, ...

The least common multiple of 12, 14, and 16 is 336. It will be 336 years before these three cicada cycles will again coincide.

C. In Question A, the answer is equal to the product of the two cycles.

In Question B, the answer is less than the product of the three cycles.

3.3 Bagging Snacks

Goals

- Recognize situations in which finding common factors of whole numbers is important

- Begin to develop strategies for finding common factors

- Observe patterns in common factors of numbers and use the patterns to reason about and predict future occurrences and solve problems

This problem is a change from the first two problems in that finding multiples gives you no useful information, but common factors are useful. Making sense of the context helps students to make the shift from common multiples to common factors.

Launch 3.3

Suggested Questions To help students focus on what you are given in the problem, you might describe a situation such as the following:

- *Seven students are going to a game. Sarah is in charge of buying snacks for the trip. Each person wants two health bars and a juice drink. How many should she buy of each?* (You multiply the number of students, 7, by 2 to get the total number of bars and by 1 to get the total number of drinks.)

- *Now in the next problem, the situation is a bit different.*

Tell them about the situation in Problem 3.3.

- *What is different in this problem from the problem I posed?* [You want the students to notice that you know the amount of food, but not the number of snack packs (people) that might be served. This is the opposite of what you know in the problem you posed.]

Give the class a minute to think about the problem. Then ask for ideas about strategies for solving the problem.

- *Let's have some discussion about where to start on solving the problem. What strategies seem appropriate?*

Here you are not trying to arrive at a single strategy for a solution, but you are trying to get some ideas on the table that students might try. Do not be afraid to leave strategies that will be counterproductive unchallenged. You will have a chance to redirect students in the Explore and Summary phases.

Let the class work in pairs. They can move into groups of four to share their ideas.

Explore 3.3

Suggested Questions Some students will try to use multiples to solve the problem. Just ask questions that point students to the context and whether their answers are reasonable in that context.

- *What are some multiples?* (72, 144, . . .)

- *Is this a reasonable answer?* (If they say yes, ask what 72 means in the context of this problem. They should see that 72 students is not a reasonable answer.)

Be sure that they identify what each number they compute means. Requiring labels for the numbers helps students reflect on whether their answers are reasonable.

Concrete-thinking students may partition 24 apples into 12 apples + 12 apples, 6 + 6 + 6 + 6, etc., so 12 represents a number of apples, and 2 + 2 + . . . + 2 represents 12 packs with 2 apples each. They need to match this with 3 + 3 + . . . + 3, representing 12 packs with 3 bags of trail mix each. Be sure they see the factor 12 as representing 12 packs with 2 apples and 12 packs with 3 bags of trail mix.

If a student is having problems, pose a simpler version of the problem.

- *Suppose Jane has 8 apples and 12 bags of trail mix. How many snack packs can she make under the conditions of the problem? Could it be 8? 12? Why?*

Going Further

- *Given any two numbers, what is the least possible number that could be the greatest common factor of the two numbers? (1) Can you find an example?*

Summarize 3.3

Suggested Questions Have several students give their solutions and their strategies. List all the common factors.

- *Which is the greatest common factor?*

- *Which part of the problem called for the greatest common factor?*

- *Which part called just for common factors?*

- *How did you know that finding factors could help?*

- *What about the problem signals that you need to analyze what numbers divide the amounts given? (Students should say something about sharing or that the answer is a number that is shared or a factor of each number.)*

When students seem comfortable with the solution, use this discussion to launch into the next problem. Problem 3.4 is similar, but uses greater numbers.

3.3 Bagging Snacks

Mathematical Goals

- Recognize situations in which finding common factors of whole numbers is important
- Begin to develop strategies for finding common factors
- Observe patterns in common factors of numbers and use the patterns to reason about and predict future occurrences and solve problems

Launch

- *Seven students are going to a game. Sarah is in charge of buying snacks for the trip. Each person wants two health bars and a juice drink. How many should she buy of each?*
- *Now in the next problem, the situation is a bit different.*

Tell them about the situation in Problem 3.3.

- *What is different in this problem from the problem I posed?*

Give the class a minute to begin thinking about the solutions to the problem. Then ask for ideas about strategies for solving the problem.

- *Let's have some discussion about where to start on solving the problem. What strategies seem appropriate?*

Don't go for a single strategy; just try to get some ideas on the table that students might try. If students offer strategies that may be counterproductive, leave them unchallenged for now. Redirect those students on the Explore and Summary phases of the lesson.

Have students work in pairs. Then move to groups of four to share their ideas.

Explore

Be sure students identify what each number they compute means. Labels help students reflect on whether their answers are reasonable.

If students try to use multiples to solve the problem, ask:

- *What are some multiples?*
- *Is this a reasonable answer?*

If they say yes, ask:

- *What does 72 mean?*

If a student is having problems, pose a simpler version of the problem.

- *Suppose Jane has 8 apples and 12 bags of trail mix. How many snack packs can she make? Could it be 8? 12? Why?*

Going Further

- *Given any two numbers, what is the least possible number that could be the greatest common factor of the two numbers? Can you find an example?*

Materials
- Calculators

continued on next page

Summarize

Have several students give their solutions and their strategies.

List all the common factors.

- *Which is the greatest common factor?*
- *Which part of the problem called for the greatest common factor?*
- *Which part called just for common factors?*
- *How did you know that finding factors could help?*
- *What in the problem signals that you need to analyze what numbers divide the amounts given? That you need to find common factors?*
- *Can a common factor ever be one of the numbers?*

Materials
- Student notebooks

ACE Assignment Guide
for Problem 3.3

Differentiated
Instruction
Solutions for All Learners

Core 16–21
Other *Applications* 22, 23; *Extensions* 39–41; unassigned choices from previous problems

Adapted For suggestions about adapting ACE exercises, see the CMP *Special Needs Handbook*.

Answers to Problem 3.3

A. 1. The greatest common factor of 24 and 36 is 12, so Jane can make 12 snack packs.

Another solution strategy is to list all of the factors of each number:

24 has 1, 2, 3, 4, 6, 8, 12, and 24 as factors.

36 has 1, 2, 3, 4, 6, 9, 12, 18, and 36 as factors.

The greatest common factor is 12. This means that each of the numbers given in the problem can be divided into 12 equal parts and thus make 12 snack packs.

2. We can see from the analysis in Question A that 24 and 36 have 1, 2, 3, 4, 6, and 12 as common factors. Therefore Jane can make 1 huge snack pack (with 24 apples and 36 bags of trail mix), 2 (12 apples, 18 bags), 3 (8 apples, 12 bags), 4 (6 apples, 9 bags), or 6 (4 apples, 6 bags), but the greatest number she can make and distribute the apples and trail mix equally is 12 (2 apples and 3 bags per pack).

3. Various answers. Many students will choose 12 because that makes more snack packs.

B. Now we have 24 apples and 30 packages of trail mix. The greatest number of snack packs Jane can make now is 6 (the greatest common factor of 24 and 30).

3.4 Planning a Picnic

Goals

- Recognize situations in which finding common factors of whole numbers is important

- Develop strategies for finding common factors and, in particular, the greatest common factor

- Recognize when common factors and greatest common factors are helpful in solving problems

This problem is different from Problem 3.3 in that it contains large numbers that depend on students being able to generalize from their experiences with Problem 3.3. One of the things that we want students to wrestle with is recognizing what signals situations where finding common multiples can be useful and what signals situations where finding common factors can be useful.

Launch 3.4

Suggested Questions Describe the new situation. Read Question A.

- *How might you solve this problem?*

Some students may continue to look for multiples because the earlier problem used multiples. If this occurs, ask some questions similar to those that were asked in the launch in Problem 3.3. That is, if they suggest a multiple, ask them what the number means. For example,

- *Is 360 a reasonable response to the question?* (If they continue to believe that 360 is a perfectly fine answer, ask them to tell you "360 what?")

- *Is "360 students" a reasonable answer to this problem?*

Remind the students that a part of problem solving is to ask oneself continually if the result seems reasonable. Labeling the results and restating the answer with the conditions of the problem helps us consider reasonableness with even more information.

Continue to ask questions to cause students to stop and think until they recognize that this problem is not one that common multiples help solve. Here what is needed is an internal analysis of the structure of the numbers involved (that is, factors), rather than an external analysis of what greater numbers this number divides.

Let the class work in pairs.

Explore 3.4

Move around the room. Some students may need some encouragement to organize their strategies for finding all the common factors.

Suggested Questions Ask:

- *What are the factors of 120? Of 90?*

- *What are the common factors of 120 and 90?*

For some students, Venn diagrams might be useful. Be sure to ask students to explain what their answer means.

- *What does the number 30 mean in the context of this problem?*

Going Further

If you think students have a good understanding of the problem and solution, ask them to think of two situations, one that calls for common multiples to find the answers, and one that calls for common factors.

Summarize 3.4

Suggested Questions After you have discussed various strategies, ask some general questions:

- *When is the greatest common factor of two numbers one of the numbers? What is special about these two numbers? Give another example that fits this pattern.*

- *When is the greatest common factor of two numbers 1? What is special about these two numbers? Give another example that fits this pattern.*

- *When is the greatest common factor of two numbers less than both numbers but greater than 1? What is special about these two numbers? Give another example that fits this pattern.*

You can use Summary Transparency 3.4 to assess where students are on their understanding of common factors and common multiples.

Summary Transparency 3.4

Jahmal has developed the following methods for finding the least common multiple and greatest common factor of two numbers.

Least Common Multiple

"To find the least common multiple, I list all the multiples of the greater number, in order, until I get a number the lesser number divides into."

1. *What do you think of Jahmal's method?* (Jahmal's method for finding the least common multiple works since he is listing the multiples in order, so he will get to the least common multiple before any other common multiples.)

2. *Why does he begin by listing the multiples of the greater number, not the lesser one?* (He starts with the greater number because that way he will have to check fewer multiples.)

Greatest Common Factor

"To find the greatest common factor, I list all the factors of the lesser number and find the greatest one that will divide into the greater number."

3. *What do you think of Jahmal's method?* (Jahmal's method for finding the greatest common factor also works because he is methodically listing factors of the lesser number.)

4. *Why does he begin by listing the factors of the lesser number, not the greater one?* (He probably starts with factors of the lesser number to have a systematic way of working

out the problem. You don't have to check the factors of both numbers, but lesser numbers do not necessarily have fewer factors.)

5. *Do you have different methods for finding the greatest common factor and the least common multiple?* (Students may have other methods. For example, one student might use the prime factorization of the two numbers to find common multiples or factors. This will be explored in Investigation 4.)

As a further summary of the ideas in this investigation, you might ask students to create a table like the one in Figure 1.

Look for patterns. Ask why a particular pattern works. Throughout this investigation, summary discussions have included questions such as, "When is the least common multiple the product of the two numbers?" and "When is the greatest common factor equal to 1?" You may want to take this time to formalize the relationships between the answers to such questions (as in the Math Background for the least common multiple in the unit opener).

Check for Understanding

You might ask students in pairs to make up a similar problem that could be solved using common factors. This will give you a good reading on whether they can differentiate problems that call for factors and those that call for multiples. An analysis of the problems they create will give the class a chance to both talk about and practice using factors to solve such problems.

You can also use the suggestion from the Going Further in the Explore section to assess their understanding.

Figure 1

First Number	Second Number	Greatest Common Factor (GCF)	Least Common Multiple (LCM)	Product of GCF and LCM	Product of the Two Numbers
12	16	4	48	$4 \times 48 = 192$	$12 \times 16 = 192$
15	30	15	30	$15 \times 30 = 450$	450
32	9	1	288	288	$32 \times 9 = 288$
45	8	1	360	360	$45 \times 8 = 360$

3.4 Planning a Picnic

Mathematical Goals

- Recognize situations in which finding common factors of whole numbers is important
- Develop strategies for finding common factors and, in particular, the greatest common factor
- Recognize when common factors and greatest common factors are helpful in solving problems

Launch

Describe the new situation and read Question A of this problem.

- *How might you solve this problem?*

If students look for multiples, ask some questions similar to those that were asked in the launch in Problem 3.3.

- *Is 360 a reasonable response to the question? 360 what? Is "360 students" a reasonable answer to this problem?*

Remind the students that a part of problem solving is to ask continually if the result seems reasonable. Labeling the result and restating the answer with the conditions of the problem helps us consider reasonableness.

Continue to ask questions that cause students to recognize that this problem is not one that common multiples help solve. What is needed here is an internal analysis of the structure of the numbers involved (that is, factors), rather than an external analysis of what greater numbers this number divides.

Have students work in pairs.

Explore

Some students may need some encouragement to organize their strategies for finding all the common factors.

- *What are the factors of 120? Of 90?*
- *What are the common factors of 120 and 90?*

For some students, Venn diagrams might be useful. Be sure to ask students to explain what their answer means.

- *What does the number 30 mean?*

Going Further

If you think students have a good understanding of the problem and solution, ask them to think of two situations, one that calls for common multiples to find the answers, and one that calls for common factors.

Materials
- Calculators

continued on next page

Summarize

After discussing the solutions and various strategies, ask general questions:

- *When is the greatest common factor of two numbers one of the numbers? What is special about these two numbers? Give another example.*

- *When is the greatest common factor of two numbers 1? What is special about these two numbers? Give another example that fits this pattern.*

- *When is the greatest common factor of two numbers less than both numbers but greater than 1? What is special about these two numbers? Give another example that fits this pattern.*

Use Summary Transparency 3.4 to assess their understanding of common factors and common multiples.

Check for Understanding

Ask pairs of students to make up a problem that could be solved using common factors. This will tell you whether they can differentiate problems that call for factors and those that call for multiples. An analysis of their problems will give the class a good chance to talk about and practice using factors to solve such problems.

Materials
- Summary Transparency 3.4
- Student notebooks

ACE Assignment Guide for Problem 3.4

Core 24–28, 30
Other *Applications* 29; *Connections* 36; *Extensions* 42–44; unassigned choices from previous problems

Adapted For suggestions about adapting Exercise 28 and other ACE exercises, see the CMP *Special Needs Handbook*.

Answers to Problem 3.4

A. 30 students could go on the trip. Each would receive 4 cans of juice and 3 packs of crackers. 30 × 4 is 120 cans of juice and 30 × 3 gives the 90 packs of crackers.

B. Now we only have 88 packs of crackers. The greatest common factor of 88 and 120 is 8. Only eight students can go on the trip, but they will be well treated! Each will receive 15 cans of juice and 11 packages of crackers.

Investigation 3

Common Multiples and Common Factors

Many things happen over and over again in fixed cycles. For example, a morning news program may have a traffic report every 7 minutes. A train may arrive at a particular station every 12 minutes. A cuckoo clock may sound every 15 minutes.

How can you figure out when two events with different cycles can occur at the same time? Thinking about common factors and common multiples can help you solve such problems.

Let's start by comparing the multiples of 20 and 30.

- The multiples of 20 are 20, 40, 60, 80, 100, 120, 140, 160, 180, . . .
- The multiples of 30 are 30, 60, 90, 120, 150, 180, . . .

The numbers 60, 120, 180, 240, . . . , are multiples of both 20 and 30. We call these numbers **common multiples** of 20 and 30. Of these multiples, 60 is the *least common multiple.*

Now let's compare the factors of 12 and 30.

- The factors of 12 are 1, 2, 3, 4, 6, and 12.
- The factors of 30 are 1, 2, 3, 5, 6, 10, 15, and 30.

The numbers 1, 2, 3, and 6, are factors of both 12 and 30. We call these numbers **common factors** of 12 and 30. Of these factors, 6 is the *greatest common factor.*

Investigation 3 Common Multiples and Common Factors **37**

Notes _____

_____

_____

_____

Riding Ferris Wheels

One of the more popular rides at a carnival or amusement park is the Ferris wheel.

Problem 3.1 Choosing Common Multiples or Common Factors

Jeremy and his little sister, Deborah, are at a carnival. There are both a large and a small Ferris wheel. Jeremy gets on the large Ferris wheel at the same time his sister gets on the small Ferris wheel. The rides begin at the same time. For each situation below, decide how many seconds will pass before Jeremy and Deborah are both at the bottom again.

A. The large wheel makes one revolution in 60 seconds and the small wheel makes one revolution in 20 seconds.

B. The large wheel makes one revolution in 50 seconds and the small wheel makes one revolution in 30 seconds.

C. The large wheel makes one revolution in 10 seconds and the small wheel makes one revolution in 7 seconds.

D. For Questions A–C, determine the number of times each Ferris wheel goes around before Jeremy and his sister are both on the ground again.

ACE Homework starts on page 42.

38 Prime Time

Notes _____

_____

_____

_____

Cicadas (si KAY dahs) spend most of their lives underground. Some populations of cicadas come above ground every 13 years, while others come up every 17 years. Although cicadas do not cause damage directly to fruits and vegetables, they can damage orchards because the female makes slits in trees to lay her eggs.

Did You Know?

Cicadas are sometimes mistakenly called locusts. A locust is actually a type of grasshopper that looks nothing like a cicada. The error originated when early European settlers in North America encountered large outbreaks of cicadas. The swarms of insects reminded the settlers of stories they knew about swarms of locusts in Egypt.

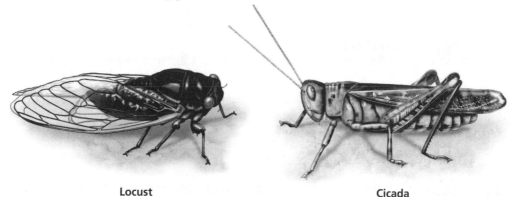

Locust   **Cicada**

Female cicadas lay their eggs in tree branches. When the young cicadas hatch, they drop to the ground and burrow into the soil. They remain underground for 13 or 17 years, feeding off juices from tree roots. Several months before they emerge, cicadas tunnel to the surface and wait to come out.

The mass emergence of cicadas is the key to their survival. There may be up to 1.5 million cicadas per acre! Many will be eaten by predators. However, enough will survive to lay eggs, so a new generation can emerge in 13 or 17 years.

Go **O**nline
PHSchool.com
For: Information about cicadas
Web Code: ame-9031

STUDENT PAGE

Notes _____

_____

_____

_____

Problem 3.2 Choosing Common Multiples or Common Factors

Stephan's grandfather told him about a terrible year when the cicadas were so numerous that they wrecked the buds on all the young trees in his orchard. Stephan conjectured that both 13-year and 17-year cicadas came up that year. Assume that Stephan's conjecture is correct.

A. How many years after an appearance of 13-year and 17-year cicadas together will both types of cicadas appear together again? Explain.

B. Suppose there were 12-year, 14-year, and 16-year cicadas, and they all came up this year. How many years will elapse before they all come up together again? Explain.

C. For Questions A and B, tell whether the answer is less than, greater than, or equal to the product of the cicada cycles.

ACE Homework starts on page 42.

3.3 Bagging Snacks

You have used common multiples to analyze events that repeat in cycles. Now you will explore problems about sharing items equally. Common factors can help you solve "sharing" problems.

Problem 3.3 Choosing Common Multiples or Common Factors

Jane and her friends are going on a hiking trip. Jane wants to make snack packs of apples and trail mix to take on the trip. She has 24 apples and 36 small bags of trail mix.

A. **1.** What is the greatest number of snack packs Jane can make if each pack must have exactly the same number of apples and exactly the same number of bags of trail mix? She doesn't want any apples or trail mix left over. Explain.

2. Could Jane make a different number of snack packs so that the treats are shared equally? If so, describe each possibility.

3. Which possibility seems most reasonable to you? Why?

Notes

B. Suppose that Jane's pet canary has bitten into six of the packages of trail mix and ruined them. Now what is the greatest number of snack packs Jane can make so that the apples and the remaining trail mix are shared equally?

 ACE Homework starts on page 42.

3.4 Planning a Picnic

Miriam's uncle runs a small convenience store. He often donates treats for Miriam's school parties.

Problem 3.4 Choosing Common Multiples or Common Factors

Miriam's uncle donated 120 cans of juice and 90 packs of cheese crackers for the school field trip. Each student is to receive the same number of cans of juice and the same number of packs of crackers.

A. What is the greatest number of students that can go on the field trip and share the food equally with no food left over? How many cans of juice and how many packs of crackers will each student receive? Explain.

B. Suppose Miriam's uncle eats two packs of crackers before he sends the supplies to school. What is the greatest number of students that can go on the field trip and share the food equally? How many cans of juice and how many packs of crackers will each student receive?

ACE Homework starts on page 42.

Notes _____

_____

_____

_____

Applications

For Exercises 1–8, list the common multiples from 1 to 100 for each pair of numbers. Then find the least common multiple for each pair.

1. 8 and 12

2. 3 and 15

3. 7 and 11

4. 9 and 10

5. 24 and 36

6. 20 and 25

7. 42 and 14

8. 30 and 12

9. a. Find three pairs of numbers for which the least common multiple equals the product of the two numbers.

    b. Look at the pairs of numbers you found in part (a). What is true about all three pairs of numbers?

For Exercises 10–13, find two pairs of numbers with the given number as their least common multiple.

10. 10

11. 36

12. 60

13. 105

14. a. A restaurant is open 24 hours a day. The manager wants to divide the day into work shifts of equal length. The shifts should not overlap, and all shift durations should be a whole number of hours. Describe the different ways this can be done.

    b. The restaurant's two neon signs are turned on at the same time. Both signs blink as they are turned on. One sign blinks every 9 seconds. The other sign blinks every 15 seconds. In how many seconds will they blink together again?

Notes _____

_____

_____

_____

15. The school cafeteria serves pizza every sixth day and applesauce every eighth day. If pizza and applesauce are both on today's menu, in how many days will they be together on the menu again?

For Exercises 16–23, list the common factors for each pair of numbers. Then find the greatest common factor for each pair.

16. 18 and 30

17. 9 and 25

18. 60 and 45

19. 23 and 29

20. 49 and 14

21. 140 and 25

22. 142 and 148

23. 84 and 105

Go Online
PHSchool.com
For: Multiple-Choice Skills Practice
Web Code: ama-1354

24. Multiple Choice For which pair is the greatest common factor 8?

A. 2 and 4

B. 7 and 15

C. 32 and 64

D. 56 and 72

25. Multiple Choice For which pair is the greatest common factor 15?

F. 60 and 75

G. 30 and 60

H. 10 and 25

J. 3 and 5

26. Multiple Choice For which pair is the greatest common factor 1?

A. 5 and 10

B. 8 and 4

C. 8 and 10

D. 8 and 15

27. Mr. Mendoza and his 23 students are planning to have hot dogs at their class picnic. Mr. Mendoza can buy hot dogs in packages of 12 and hot dog buns in packages of 8.

Homework
Help Online
PHSchool.com
For: Help with Exercise 27
Web Code: ame-1327

a. Mr. Mendoza plans that everyone will get the same number of hot dogs and buns and there will be no leftovers. What are the least number of hot dog packages and the least number of bun packages Mr. Mendoza can buy? How many hot dogs and buns will each person get?

b. Suppose that the class invites the principal, the secretary, the bus driver, and three parents to help supervise. How many packages of hot dogs and buns will Mr. Mendoza need to buy so that everyone will get the same number of hot dogs and buns with no leftovers? How many hot dogs and buns will each person get?

Investigation 3 Common Multiples and Common Factors **43**

Notes _____

_____

_____

_____

28. The cast of a play had a party at the drama teacher's house. There were 20 cookies and 40 carrot sticks served as refreshments. Each cast member had the same number of whole cookies and the same number of whole carrot sticks. Nothing was left over. The drama teacher did not eat. How many cast members might have been at the party? Explain.

29. Make up a word problem that you can solve by finding common factors. Then make up a different word problem that you can solve by finding common multiples. Solve your problems, and explain how you know that your answers are correct.

30. Multiple Choice Neena has 54 smiley-face stickers, 36 glittery stickers, and 81 heart stickers. She wants to divide the stickers evenly among her friends. Find the greatest number that Neena can use to divide the stickers evenly.

F. 3   **G.** 9   **H.** 18   **J.** 27

Connections

31. Use the terms *factor, divisor, multiple, product,* and *divisible by* to write as many statements as you can about the number sentence below.

$$7 \times 9 = 63$$

32. a. What factor is paired with 12 to give 48?

    b. What factor is paired with 11 to give 110?

33. Use the fact that $135 \times 37 = 4{,}995$ to find the value of $1{,}350 \times 3{,}700$.

34. a. Suppose a jet travels 60 kilometers in 5 minutes. How many kilometers will it travel in 2 hours? In 6 hours?

    b. How many more kilometers will the jet travel in 6 hours than in 2 hours?

    c. Suppose that Nodin flew on this jet to the Dominican Republic. If his trip took 4 hours, how many kilometers did he travel?

35. Mario's watch runs fast. In 1 day, it gains an hour; so in 12 days, it gains 12 hours and is correct again. Julio's watch also runs fast. In 1 day, it gains 20 minutes. If they both set their 12-hour watches correctly at 9:00 A.M. on Monday, when will their watches both be correct again at the same time?

Notes _____

_____

_____

_____

36. 3 × 5 × 7 = 105. Use this fact to find each product.

   a. 9 × 5 × 7   **b.** 3 × 5 × 14

   c. 3 × 50 × 7   **d.** 3 × 25 × 7

Extensions

37. Ms. Santiago has many pens in her desk drawer. She says that if you divide the total number of pens by 2, 3, 4, 5, or 6, you get a remainder of 1. What is the smallest number of pens that could be in Ms. Santiago's drawer?

38. What is the mystery number pair?

   Clue 1 The greatest common factor of the mystery pair is 7.

   Clue 2 The least common multiple of the mystery pair is 70.

   Clue 3 Both of the numbers in the mystery pair have two digits.

   Clue 4 One of the numbers in the mystery pair is odd and the other is even.

39. Suppose that, in some distant part of the universe, there is a star with four orbiting planets. One planet makes a trip around the star in 6 Earth years, the second planet takes 9 Earth years, the third takes 15 Earth years, and the fourth takes 18 Earth years. Suppose that at some time the planets are lined up as pictured below. This phenomenon is called *conjunction*. How many years will it take before the planets return to this position?

Notes _____

_____

_____

_____

40. Eric and his friends practice multiplying by using dominoes such as those above. Each half of a domino has dots on it to show a number from 0 to 6. The students use the two numbers on a domino as factors. So when Eric sees a domino like the one below, he answers 12.

    a. What is the greatest product you can make from numbers on dominoes?

    b. What is the least product you can make from numbers on dominoes?

    c. Eric reasons that he has to know the answers for $0 \times 0, 0 \times 1,$ $0 \times 2, 0 \times 3, 0 \times 4, 0 \times 5, 0 \times 6, 1 \times 0, 1 \times 1,$ and so on. Because there are seven different numbers, 0, 1, 2, 3, 4, 5, and 6, that can occur on each half of the domino, he reasons that he needs to know 49 different answers. This is too many. What did he forget?

41. Examine the number pattern below. You can use the tiles to help you see a pattern.

Row 1: 1   = 1

Row 2: 1 + 3   = 4

Row 3: 1 + 3 + 5   = 9

Row 4: 1 + 3 + 5 + 7 = 16

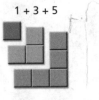

    a. Complete the next four rows in the number pattern.

    b. What is the sum in row 20?

    c. In what row will the sum be 576? What is the last number (addend) in the sum in this row? Explain.

Notes _____

_____

_____

_____

42. Examine the pattern below. Using tiles or making a diagram may help you see a pattern.

Row 1: 2   = 2

Row 2: 2 + 4   = 6

Row 3: 2 + 4 + 6   = 12

Row 4: 2 + 4 + 6 + 8 = 20

  a. Complete the next four rows in the pattern.

  b. What is the sum in row 20?

  c. In what row will the sum be 110? What is the last number (addend) in the sum in this row? Explain.

43. a. Suppose that cicadas have predators with 2-year cycles. How often would 12-year cicadas face their predators? Would life be better for 13-year cicadas? Explain.

  b. Suppose that 12-year and 13-year cicadas have predators with both 2-year and 3-year cycles. Suppose that both kinds of cicadas and both kinds of predators came up this year. When would the 12-year cicadas again have to face both kinds of predators at the same time? When would the 13-year cicadas face both? Which type of cicada do you think is better off?

"BELIEVE ME, THEY'RE NOT EXPECTING US. WE'RE 387-YEAR LOCUSTS."

44. While Nina was reading through her old journals, she noticed that on November 9, 1999, she had written the date 11-9-99. It looked like a multiplication problem, $11 \times 9 = 99$. Nina wondered if there were any other such dates from 1900 to 1999. Are there? Explain.

Notes _____

_____

_____

_____

Mathematical Reflections 3

In this investigation, you used common factors and common multiples to help you solve problems. These questions will help you summarize what you have learned.

Think about your answers to these questions. Discuss your ideas with other students and your teacher. Then write a summary of your findings in your notebook.

1. Look at the four problems in this investigation. Explain how you can decide if finding common multiples or common factors is helpful in solving a problem.

2. Describe how you can find the common factors and the greatest common factor of two numbers.

3. Describe how you can find the common multiples and the least common multiple of two numbers.

Unit Project   What's Next?

Don't forget to write about your special number!

Notes _____

_____

_____

_____

Investigation

ACE Assignment Choices

Differentiated Instruction
Solutions for All Learners

Problem 3.1
Core 1–5, 31, 32
Other *Applications* 6–8

Problem 3.2
Core 10, 11, 15
Other *Applications* 9, 12–14; *Connections* 33–35; *Extensions* 37, 38; unassigned choices from previous problems

Problem 3.3
Core 16–21
Other *Applications* 22, 23; *Extensions* 39–41; unassigned choices from previous problems

Problem 3.4
Core 24–28, 30
Other *Applications* 29, *Connections* 36, *Extensions* 42–44; unassigned choices from previous problems

Adapted For suggestions about adapting Exercise 28 and other ACE exercises, see the CMP *Special Needs Handbook*.
Connecting to Prior Units 32: elementary school multiplication algorithms

Applications

1. 24, 48, 72, and 96; the least common multiple is 24.
2. 15, 30, 45, 60, 75, and 90; the least common multiple is 15.
3. 77; the least common multiple is 77.
4. 90; the least common multiple is 90.
5. 72; the least common multiple is 72.
6. 100; the least common multiple is 100.
7. 42, 84; the least common multiple is 42.

8. 60; the least common multiple is 60.
9. **a.** Possible answers: 3, 5; 8, 9; 7, 11
   b. They have no common factors except 1.
10. Possible answers: 2, 5; 1, 10
11. Possible answers: 4, 9; 18, 36
12. Possible answers: 4, 15; 12, 5
13. Possible answers: 3, 35; 7, 15
14. **a.** Twenty-four 1-hour shifts; twelve 2-hour shifts; eight 3-hour shifts; six 4-hour shifts; four 6-hour shifts; three 8-hour shifts; two 12-hour shifts, and one 24-hour shift. These are all factors of 24.
    b. 45 seconds, which is the least common multiple of 9 and 15
15. 24 days
16. 1, 2, 3, and 6; the greatest common factor is 6.
17. 1; the greatest common factor is 1.
18. 1, 3, 5, and 15; the greatest common factor is 15.
19. 1 is the only common factor.
20. 1, 7; the greatest common factor is 7.
21. 1, 5; the greatest common factor is 5.
22. 1, 2; the greatest common factor is 2.
23. 1, 3, 7, 21; the greatest common factor is 21.
24. D   25. F   26. D
27. **a.** 2 packages of hot dogs and 3 packages of buns; 1 hot dog and 1 bun
    b. 10 packages of hot dogs and 15 packages of buns; 4 hot dogs and 4 buns
28. 20: each gets 1 cookie and 2 carrot sticks
    10: each gets 2 cookies and 4 carrot sticks
    5: each gets 4 cookies and 8 carrot sticks
    4: each gets 5 cookies and 10 carrot sticks
    2: each gets 10 cookies and 20 carrot sticks
    1: gets it all: 20 cookies and 40 carrot sticks

29. Answers will vary. For example, a problem using common factors might be: "The Morgan family buys a 12-pack of bottled water and a 24-pack of boxes of raisins. Each person in the family gets the same number of bottles of water and the same number of boxes of raisins. How many people might there be in the Morgan family?" The Morgan family could have 1, 2, 3, 4, 6, or 12 people. I know I'm right because these numbers are common factors of 12 and 24. An example of a problem using common multiples is: "John eats an apple once a week. Ruth eats an apple every third day. If they both eat an apple today, when will John and Ruth next eat an apple on the same day?" John and Ruth will both eat apples on the same day in 21 days. I know I'm right because this problem involves overlapping cycles, so it can be solved with common multiples.

30. G

Connections

31. 7 is a factor of 63. 9 is a factor of 63. 7 is a divisor of 63. 9 is a divisor of 63. The product of 7 and 9 is 63. The product of 9 and 7 is 63. 63 is divisible by 7. 63 is divisible by 9. 63 is a multiple of 7. 63 is a multiple of 9.

32. a. 4   **b.** 10

33. 4,995,000; add 3 zeros for the three factors of 10.

34. a. In 2 hours, the jet will travel $12 \times 2 \times 60 = 1{,}440$ kilometers. In 6 hours, the jet will travel $1{,}440 \times 3 = 4{,}320$ kilometers.

     b. In 6 hours, the jet will travel $4{,}320 - 1{,}440 = 2{,}880$ kilometers more than in 2 hours.

     c. In 4 hours, he would travel twice as many miles as in 2 hours, or 2,880 kilometers.

35. Students need to be able to reason proportionally (without knowing that vocabulary) to move from 20 minutes in 1 day to 1 hour in 3 days to 12 hours in 36 days. Julio gains 12 hours in 36 days. Since 12 is a factor of 36, both watches will be correct again 36 days after they set the watches, or at 9:00 A.M. on the 6th Tuesday.

36. This question also asks students to reason proportionally.

     a. $9 \times 5 \times 7$ will be 3 times as great as $3 \times 5 \times 7$, so 315.

     b. $3 \times 5 \times 14$ will be twice as great as $3 \times 5 \times 7$, so 210.

     c. $3 \times 50 \times 7$ will be 10 times as great as $3 \times 5 \times 7$, so 1,050.

     d. $3 \times 25 \times 7$ will be 5 times as great as $3 \times 5 \times 7$, so 525.

Extensions

37. $3 \times 4 \times 5 + 1 = 61$ (Find the least common multiple of 2, 3, 4, 5, and 6, and add 1.)

38. 14 and 35   **39.** 90 years

40. a. 36   **b.** 0

     c. Eric forgot that $3 \times 4 = 4 \times 3$. (Multiplication is commutative.)

41. a. $1 + 3 + 5 + 7 + 9 = 25$;
$1 + 3 + 5 + 7 + 9 + 11 = 36$;
$1 + 3 + 5 + 7 + 9 + 11 + 13 = 49$;
$1 + 3 + 5 + 7 + 9 + 11 + 13 + 15 = 64$

     b. $1 + 3 + 5 + \ldots + 39 = 20^2 = 400$

     c. Row 24; 47. The sum will be 576 in row 24, because 576 is 24^2. The last number in this row is 47 because 47 is the twenty-fourth odd number. (This famous pattern is the sum of the consecutive odd numbers: the sum in each row is the square of the number of numbers in the row.)

42. a. Tiles can be used to set up a visual display of this problem. From the pattern, you can see that adding the first n consecutive even numbers is the same as multiplying n times $(n + 1)$. So, the next four rows are as follows:

$2 + 4 + 6 + 8 + 10 = 30$ (which is 5×6)

$2 + 4 + 6 + 8 + 10 + 12 = 42$ (which is 6×7)

$2 + 4 + 6 + 8 + 10 + 12 + 14 = 56$
(which is 7×8)

$2 + 4 + 6 + 8 + 10 + 12 + 14 + 16 = 72$
(which is 8×9)

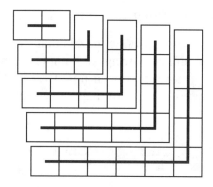

b. $2 + 4 + 6 + \ldots + 40 = 420$
(which is 20×21)

c. Row 10 since $10 \times 11 = 110$; 20 because 20 is the tenth even number.

43. a. 12-year cicadas would meet 2-year predators either every time they emerge or never. The 13-year cicadas would encounter predators every other time they emerge, so they could be better or worse off depending on whether the predator came out on odd or even years.

b. The 12-year cicadas will meet both types of predators every time they emerge. The

13-year cicadas will meet the 2-year predators every other time they emerge, and the 3-year predators every third time they emerge. This means that it will be 6 cycles or 78 years before the 13-year locusts have to face both predators again. They are better off than the 12-year cicadas.

44. Yes; there are 212 dates like this. (Figure 2)

Possible Answers to Mathematical Reflections

1. In the first two problems, it was helpful to find common multiples. In the last two problems, it was helpful to find common factors. When the problem involves the repetitions of two or more events and asks questions about when the events will be in sync, then you need to find common multiples. When the problem involves sharing different amounts equally, common factors will help.

2. List the factors for each number and then find the factors that are in both lists. Of these numbers, choose the greatest.

3. List several multiples for each number and then look for the numbers that are in both lists. Of these numbers, choose the least.

Figure 2

Month	Day	Last Two Digits of the Year	Number of Dates
01	01–31	01, 02, 03, 04, 05, 06, 07, 08, 09, 10, 11, 12, 13, . . . , 31	31
02	01–28	02, 04, 06, 08, 10, 12, 14, 16, 18, 20, 22, 24, 26, . . . , 56	28
03	01–31	03, 06, 09, 12, 15, 18, 21, 24, 27, 30, 33, 36, 39, . . . , 93	31
04	01–24	04, 08, 12, 16, 20, 24, 28, . . . , 96 Note: 04 × 25 ≠ 00	24
05	01–19	05, 10, 15, 20, 25, 30, 35 . . . , 95 Note: 05 × 20 ≠ 00	19
06	01–16	06, 12, 18, 24, 30, 36, 42, 48, 54, 60, 66, 72, 78, . . . , 96	16
07	01–14	07, 14, 21, 28, 35, 42, 49, 56, 63, 70, 77, 84, 91, 98	14
08	01–12	08, 16, 24, 32, 40, 48, 56, 64, 72, 80, 88, 96	12
09	01–11	09, 18, 27, 36, 45, 54, 63, 72, 81, 90, 99	11
10	01–09	10, 20, 30, 40, 50, 60, 70, 80, 90 Note: 10 × 10 ≠ 00	9
11	01–09	11, 22, 33, 44, 55, 66, 77, 88, 99	9
12	01–08	12, 24, 36, 48, 60, 72, 84, 96	8
		Total Number of Dates	212

Investigation 4 Factorizations: Searching for Factor Strings

Mathematical and Problem-Solving Goals

- Find factorizations of numbers and then break them down into prime factorizations

- Understand that prime numbers are the essential multiplicative building blocks for whole numbers

- Develop a systematic strategy for finding prime factorizations

- Recognize that a number may have several different factorizations but, except for order, each whole number greater than 1 has exactly one factorization into a product of prime numbers (the Fundamental Theorem of Arithmetic)

- Find common factors, greatest common factors, common multiples, and least common multiples using prime factorizations

Summary of Problems

Problem 4.1 The Product Puzzle

Students explore a product puzzle that shows the existence of multiple strings of numbers forming factorizations for a particular number, 840. The question raised is about finding longer and longer strings.

Problem 4.2 Finding the Longest Factor String

Students work on finding the "longest" strings of factors that form a factorization. This leads to breaking non-prime numbers into primes and recognizing that the process ends when all of the numbers in the factorization are prime. The students choose from two strategies to find prime factorizations. They begin to see that not only is this factorization unique, but it can be used to find other information about the number.

Problem 4.3 Using Prime Factorizations

Students apply prime factorizations to finding greatest common factors and least common multiples.

	Suggested Pacing	Materials for Students	Materials for Teachers	ACE Assignments
All	$3\frac{1}{2}$ days	Calculators; colored pens, pencils, or markers; blank transparencies and transparency markers (optional: for recording results); student notebooks	Blank transparencies and transparency markers	
4.1	1 day	Labsheet 4.1 (1 per student)	Transparencies 4.1A and 4.1B	1–3, 25, 26, 34
4.2	1 day		Transparency 4.2	4–18, 27–30, 35
4.3	1 day		Transparency 4.3	19–24, 31–33, 36
MR	$\frac{1}{2}$ day			

The Product Puzzle

Goals

- Find factorizations of numbers and then break them down into prime factorizations

- Understand that prime numbers are the essential multiplicative building blocks for whole numbers

This section provokes students to think about factorizations of whole numbers. In previous investigations, students have been in many situations where they needed to find the factor pairs for given numbers. Each factor pair gives a factorization of the number. Now students will extend their understanding of the factorizations of a number to include looking beyond factor pairs to find factor strings of different lengths for a given number. Students find that a given number may have several factor strings, or factorizations, of differing lengths (two factors, three factors, four factors, etc.).

Launch 4.1

Launch this problem by helping students to move from thinking about factor pairs to thinking about longer strings of factors.

Suggested Questions Use as much of the following as your students need to move beyond thinking only in terms of factor pairs:

- *So far in this unit, we have looked at factor pairs of given numbers. For example, we can express 24 as 4 × 6, 2 × 12, or 3 × 8.*

- *Can you think of three numbers you can multiply to get a product of 24?*

If students suggest a string containing a 1, such as 1 × 2 × 12, ask them to suggest a different string:

- *Can you find three numbers that do not include the number 1?* (Students may give the strings 4 × 3 × 2 or 2 × 2 × 6.)

- *Can you find a different string of three numbers?* (Students may say they can find another by listing the factors in a

different order, such as 3 × 2 × 4. Let them know that order does not determine whether it is a different string. The factors used are what matters.)

- *Let's look at a greater number because it might be more interesting. How about 360? What numbers can you multiply to get a product of 360?*

Write the strings that students give you on the board, organizing them by the number of factors they contain. If students give only strings of two numbers, ask for strings of three numbers. If you get answers like 3 × 120 × 1, show them that this isn't really different from 3 × 120 × 1 × 1 × 1 × 1 × 1 × 1 × 1. We want them to see that the number 1 in a factorization gives no new information, so we won't consider this in the factorizations.

- *We are going to continue searching for strings that are factorizations of the number. Try to get longer and longer factor strings in the Product Puzzle.*

- *The question you want to think about is how do you know when you have found the longest possible string? For example, how do you know you cannot make a string for 360 with more numbers in it than any of the strings we recorded on the board?* (Do not look for a definitive answer from students at this time. This is a question for students to consider as they work on the puzzle. The fact that the longest string for 360 contains only prime numbers will probably not come up yet, but the puzzle will give them an opportunity to find this out for themselves.)

The Getting Ready also offers another example:

- *Can you find a longer string of factors with a product of 100?* [The longest string of factors of 100 (not including 1) is 2 × 2 × 5 × 5. This is the prime factorization.]

Give each student a copy of Labsheet 4.1. On Transparency 4.1, demonstrate how to mark strings of numbers on the labsheet and record each string at the bottom of the labsheet. The

Student Edition shows two examples. Students need to understand that the strings can be marked from any set of connected numbers. The numbers can be any combination of numbers that are located above, below, next to, or diagonal to each other. You can either show some examples of these or let the students find what makes sense.

Students should work alone on the puzzle for about 5 minutes, then pair up, share findings, and continue the search for a few more minutes.

If a student is anxious about listing a string already on the board but with a different ordering of the factors, either ask whether that string has already been listed, or allow it to be added to the list to stimulate a conversation about the ordering of factors.

Explore 4.1

You might make the game more interesting by setting a timer to see how many strings students can find in 4 minutes. Ask students to record the factors of the strings they are circling. As you circulate, continue to ask whether they can find a longer string than one they have.

You may want to have recording going on as the students find strings. If so, ask students to go to the board and list the strings they have found in the appropriate columns. (Figure 1)

Summarize 4.1

From the table, we have many possibilities for exploration. One teacher used a color scheme to explore relationships between the factor strings. She circled each string with two factors in a different color and then used the same color to indicate when a longer string could be obtained by decomposing a given shorter string. For example, she might circle 420×2 in green and 280×3 in blue. Then she could circle $210 \times 2 \times 2$ in green and $15 \times 28 \times 2$ in green and $140 \times 2 \times 3$ in blue. Eventually $5 \times 2 \times 2 \times 3 \times 2 \times 7$ would be circled in all the different colors, because this string is a decomposition of *every* string on the table.

Figure 1

Strings With Two Factors	Strings With Three Factors	Strings With Four Factors	Strings With Five Factors	Strings With Six Factors	Strings With Seven Factors
420 × 2	210 × 2 × 2	21 × 2 × 4 × 5	7 × 5 × 4 × 3 × 2	5 × 2 × 2 × 3 × 2 × 7	
280 × 3	40 × 3 × 7	20 × 2 × 3 × 7			
210 × 4	5 × 42 × 4				
168 × 5	4 × 3 × 70				
140 × 6					
120 × 7					
105 × 8					
84 × 10					
70 × 12					
60 × 14					
56 × 15					
42 × 20					
40 × 21					
35 × 24					
30 × 28					

Suggested Questions Ask students to look carefully at the strings on the board.

• *Do you think we need to revise any of the strings on the board? If so, why?*

Have students put a check or some mark near the strings they think are wrong. Then, as a whole class, discuss the strings in question. This may be an opportunity to discuss that ordering of the factors does not create a new string. Students may discuss that they can mark the entries of some of the strings in different orders on the puzzle. For example, you might generate a string by moving to a number that is adjacent on the horizontal row then to a number directly above the new entry or by moving on the diagonal then down to get the two new numbers in a different order. Either way they get the same factors in the string just in a different order.

• *Are there other strings of factors for 840 that we could add to our lists?* (By looking at the list, students may see patterns and record some string not in the puzzle.)

• *The longest string we listed here has _____ factors. Can you find a longer string? Why or why not?*

• *Look at one of the strings with two factors. Can you see how it relates to one of the strings with three factors?* (There are many possibilities here. One example is, a student may pick 210 × 4 and say that you can think of a factor pair of 210, like 21 × 10. So, you could get the string 21 × 10 × 4 by breaking down the factor 210.)

• *Can you explain how a string with three factors relates to a string with four factors?* (Again, there are many possibilities. We want

students to see that you can take a string with three factors and decompose one of the factors to get a longer string.)

• *Could we go the other way? Can we use a string of four factors to get a string of three factors? How?* (Yes, we could multiply two of the factors together; that would give us a string with three factors. For example, with the string 20 × 2 × 3 × 7, we could multiply the 3 × 7 to get 21 and the new string of three factors would be 20 × 2 × 21.)

Continue asking students to relate the strings of one length to the strings of another length, until you get to the uniqueness of the longest string.

• *Look at one of the strings with five factors. Can you use it to get a string with six factors?* (Yes, we could take 7 × 5 × 4 × 3 × 2 and rewrite the 4 as 2 × 2 to get a factor string of 7 × 5 × 2 × 2 × 3 × 2.)

• *Can we keep going and get a string with seven factors?* (No, because all the numbers are prime. We cannot take any of those numbers and break them apart into any factor pairs except 1 times the number. We said we were not going to use 1.)

• *How do you know when you have found the longest possible string of factors for a number?* (If all the numbers in a string are prime, the string is the longest possible. No further decomposition is possible.)

• *This longest string of factors made up of all prime numbers has a special name. It is called the* prime factorization *of the number.*

This terminology is in the introduction to Problem 4.2 in the Student Edition.

4.1 The Product Puzzle

Mathematical Goals

- Find factorizations of numbers and then break them down into prime factorizations
- Understand that prime numbers are the essential multiplicative building blocks for whole numbers

Launch

Help students move from thinking about factor pairs to thinking about longer strings of factors.

- *So far in this unit, we have looked at factor pairs of given numbers. For example, we can express 24 as 4 × 6, 2 × 12, or 3 × 8. Can you think of three numbers you can multiply to get a product of 24?*
- *What numbers can you multiply to get a product of 360?*

Record the strings, organizing them by the number of factors. Help them to see that 1 gives no new information, so we won't use it in the factorizations.

- *We are going to continue searching for strings that are factorizations. Try to get longer and longer factor strings in the Product Puzzle. As you work on the puzzle, think about this question: "How do you know when you have found the longest possible string?"*

Demonstrate how to mark and record strings of numbers on the Labsheet 4.1.

Students should work alone on the puzzle for about 5 minutes, then pair up, share findings, and continue the search for a few more minutes.

Materials
- Transparencies 4.1A and 4.1B

Vocabulary
- factorization

Explore

As you circulate, continue to ask whether they can find a longer string than the one they have.

Have students go to the board and list the strings they have found in columns labeled by the number of factors in the string.

Materials
- Labsheet 4.1

Summarize

From the table, there are many possibilities for exploration. One idea is to use a color scheme to explore relationships between the strings. Eventually 5 × 2 × 2 × 3 × 2 × 7 would be circled in all of the different colors because this string is a decomposition of *every* string on the table.

- *Do you think we need to revise any of the strings on the board? Why?*

As a class, discuss the strings in question. This may be an opportunity to discuss that ordering of the factors does not create a new string.

- *Are there other strings of factors for 840 that we could add to our lists?*

Materials
- Student notebooks

Vocabulary
- prime factorization
- distinct

continued on next page

- *Look at one of the strings with two factors. Can you see how it relates to one of the strings with three factors? Can you explain how a string with three factors relates to a string with four factors?*

- *Could we go the other way? Can we use a string of four factors to get a string of three factors? How?*

Continue asking students to relate the strings of one length to the strings of another length, until you get to the uniqueness of the longest string.

- *Look at one of the strings with five factors. Can you use it to get a string with six factors? Can we keep going and get a string with seven factors?*

- *How do you know when you have found the longest possible string of factors for a number?*

- *This longest string of factors made up of all prime numbers has a special name. It is called the* prime factorization *of the number.*

ACE Assignment Guide for Problem 4.1

Core 1–3, 25
Other *Connections* 26, *Extensions* 34

Adapted For suggestions about adapting Exercises 1–3 and other ACE exercises, see the CMP *Special Needs Handbook.*

Answers to Problem 4.1

A. Answers will vary, but the longest string in the puzzle is $2 \times 2 \times 2 \times 3 \times 5 \times 7$.

B. It is not possible to find a longer string than is in the puzzle. It may of course be possible for a student to find a longer string than he or she *found* in the puzzle. The longest possible string is $2 \times 2 \times 2 \times 3 \times 5 \times 7$.

C. Some strings can be decomposed to get longer strings. For example, 420×2 can be split up into $210 \times 2 \times 2$.

D. If all the numbers in a string are prime, the string is the longest possible. No further decomposition is possible.

E. Except for order, every whole number has exactly one longest string.

4.2 Finding the Longest Factor String

Goals

- Develop a systematic strategy for finding prime factorizations

- Recognize that a number may have several different factorizations but, except for order, each whole number greater than 1 has exactly one factorization into a product of prime numbers (the Fundamental Theorem of Arithmetic)

This section provides further opportunity for students to develop an understanding of prime factorization and to develop a systematic strategy for finding the prime factorization of a number.

In Problem 4.1, students thought about the factor strings and the existence and uniqueness of prime factorizations. In this section they develop a systematic way for finding the prime factorizations. They begin to see that this unique factorization can be used to find other information about the number.

Launch 4.2

Students may choose from two methods to find factorizations. Discuss them both.

Method 1: Division

You can launch this problem by referring to Problem 4.1.

- *Yesterday we found the longest string of factors for 840. How could we communicate our method to someone else?* (We decomposed numbers into longer and longer strings of factors until we found the longest string, which turned out to be made up of all prime numbers.)

- *Let's look at a systematic way to find the longest factor string for 360. We know we are interested in finding all the prime factors. So, can anyone tell me one prime factor of 360?*

If a student suggests the prime number 2, for example, ask for the corresponding factor pair. Write this as you would a division problem. Continue by asking for a prime factor of 180 and the corresponding factor pair.

```
2 | 360
2 | 180
3 | 90
2 | 30
5 | 15
    3
```

Continue breaking down the factors until the result is a prime number. This is the division method.

Method 2: Factor Trees

This method is useful because it suggests "breaking apart" numbers into their factor pairs and subsequently "breaking apart" the factors. Below we show this method for 360, although you can delay working on this until the summary transparency at the end of this problem.

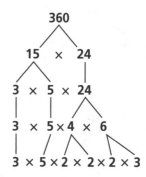

Students might develop a similar method on their own. If some students are having difficulty finding the longest (prime) factorization of a number, you might want to lead them to this method. The methods are equally valid, so students should use the one that makes the most sense to them.

- *Another way to find the longest factorization of a number is to make a factor tree. This is similar to how we looked at strings of factors when we discussed the Product Puzzle. What is a factor pair of 360?*

Students may suggest different factor pairs. Begin with a few of them to show that it does not matter which factor pair you begin with.

- *We have several examples of factor pairs of 360.*

For example, show 360 with branches to 36×10, show 360 with branches to 2×180, and show 360 with branches to 15×24.

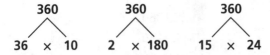

- *Do we have the prime factorization of 360?* (No, these are not the longest strings because some of the numbers in the strings are not prime.)

- *Let's look at the individual factors and see if we can break any of them into factor pairs and get closer to having all the prime factors of 360.*

Continue with the discussion so students see three examples of using a factor tree strategy to find the prime factorization of 360. (Figure 2)

- *What is the prime factorization of 360?* ($2 \times 3 \times 2 \times 3 \times 2 \times 5$)

- *When we have a long string of primes, we usually write them in order from least to greatest. So we would write the prime factorization of 360 as $2 \times 2 \times 2 \times 3 \times 3 \times 5$.*

- *You can use a shorthand notation to write prime factorizations. For example, you can write $2 \times 2 \times 2 \times 3 \times 3 \times 5$ as $2^3 \times 3^2 \times 5$. The small raised number is called an* exponent. *An exponent tells you how many times the factor is used. For example, $2^2 \times 5^4$ means the 2 is used twice and the 5 is used four times. So, $2^2 \times 5^4$ is the same as $2 \times 2 \times 5 \times 5 \times 5 \times 5$. The notation 2^3 is read "2 to the third power."*

Give students the challenge to find prime factorizations and answer the other questions in the problem.

Let them work alone and then compare their answers with a partner.

Explore 4.2

Allow students some time to work individually on determining the prime factorizations of 72 and 120.

If needed, show the work of some students on the board.

Suggested Questions

- *Did everyone in your group get the same prime factorization?* (Yes.)

If some students say no, ask some questions to see where they are struggling. These are the kinds of questions students should ask themselves as they determine prime factorizations.

- *Are all the numbers in your string prime?*

Figure 2

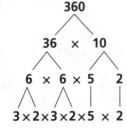
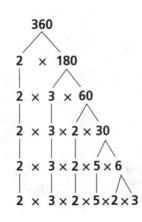
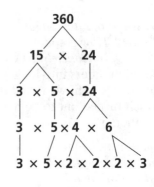

- *Did you keep track of all the prime factors as you found them?*

- *Did you multiply your string of numbers to see if the product was 72? Or 120?*

Students need to recognize that no matter what prime factor they started with, they will get the same string of prime factors since order doesn't matter. Give them time to finish the problem.

Summarize 4.2

Select a student to present his or her strategy and the factor string he or she found for 600.

Suggested Questions

- *Did anyone use a different strategy or get a different result?*

If a student suggests a string that differs only in the order of the factors, ask if the string should really be considered different.

- *How can we rewrite the prime factorization of 600 using exponents?* ($2^3 \times 3 \times 5^2$)

Leave the correct prime factorization on the board so you can refer to it later.

Select two more pairs to present the prime factorizations for 72 and 120.

- *How can we rewrite the prime factorization of 72 using exponents?* ($2^3 \times 3^2$) *Of 120 using exponents?* ($2^3 \times 3 \times 5$)

- *Do we all need to use the same strategy to find the prime factorization of a number?* (No, because either way you end up finding all the prime factors of the number. With one strategy you are thinking of prime factors as divisors. With the other strategy you are finding ways to replace an existing factor with a factor pair, making longer and longer strings until all the factors are prime.)

Students should now see that the longest factorization of a number is the prime factorization and that this factorization is unique. It is called the Fundamental Theorem of Arithmetic. You might want to keep asking questions until this point is clear. The students will have more opportunities to think about this in the ACE exercises.

- *Name a non-prime factor of 72. What is the prime factorization of that non-prime factor?* (There are various possibilities; one example would be $6 = 2 \times 3$.)

- *Is it contained in* $2 \times 2 \times 2 \times 3 \times 3$, *the prime factorization of 72?* (Yes, one example would be to underline the 2×3 in the prime factorization: $2 \times 2 \times \underline{2 \times 3} \times 3$)

- *Using the prime factorization of 72, how can we determine the factor that pairs with your number to equal 72?* (6, or $\underline{2 \times 3}$, would be paired with $2 \times 2 \times 3$, or 12, to equal 72.)

Make sure students see that the entire prime factorization of 72 contains the prime factorization of both numbers in the factor pair.

- *What will the prime factorization of a multiple of 72 have in common with the prime factorization of 72?* (The prime factorization of a multiple of 72 will include the prime factorization of 72 plus the other prime numbers it was multiplied by to get the multiple. For example, 288 is a multiple of 72 because $72 \times 4 = 288$. We can rewrite 72 as $2 \times 2 \times 2 \times 3 \times 3$ and we can rewrite 4 as $\underline{2 \times 2}$. So the prime factorization of 288 is $2 \times 2 \times 2 \times 3 \times 3 \times \underline{2 \times 2}$.)

Make sure students see that *every* multiple of 72 will have a prime factorization that entirely contains the prime factorization of 72.

INVESTIGATION 4

4.2 Finding the Longest Factor String

Mathematical Goals

- Develop a systematic strategy for finding prime factorizations
- Recognize that a number may have several different factorizations but, except for order, each whole number greater than 1 has exactly one factorization into a product of prime numbers (the Fundamental Theorem of Arithmetic)

Launch

Method 1: Division

- *Let's look at a systematic way to find the longest factor string for 360. Can anyone tell me one prime factor of 360?*

Write this as a division problem. Continue asking for prime factors of 180 (assuming students answered above with "2") and breaking down the factors until the result is a prime number.

Method 2: Factor Trees

- *Another way is to make a factor tree. What is a factor pair of 360?*

Begin with a few factor pairs to show that it does not matter where you begin.

- *Let's look at the individual factors and decompose them to get all the prime factors of 360.*

Continue the three examples to show how to find the prime factorization of 360.

- *What is the prime factorization of 360? We usually write a long string of primes in order: $2 \times 2 \times 2 \times 3 \times 3 \times 5$. You can use shorthand notation and rewrite this: $2^3 \times 3^2 \times 5$. The small raised number, an exponent, tells you how many times the factor is used. 2^3 is read "2 to the third power."*

Let them work alone and then compare their answers with a partner.

Materials

- Transparency 4.2

Vocabulary

- exponent
- factorization
- prime factorization

Explore

If needed, stop and share strategies for finding the factorizations of 72 and 120.

- *Did everyone in your group get the same prime factorization?*

Students should ask themselves questions as they work. Model by asking them:

- *Are all the numbers in your string prime?*
- *Did you keep track of all the prime factors as you found them?*
- *Did you multiply your string of numbers to see if the product was 72?*

Summarize

Select a student to show his/her strategy and the factor string found for 600.

- *Did anyone use a different strategy or get a different result?*
- *How can we rewrite the prime factorization of 600 using exponents?*

Select two more to present the prime factorizations for 72 and 120.

- *How can we rewrite those prime factorizations using exponents?*
- *Do we all need to use the same strategy?*

Students should now see that the longest factorization of a number is the prime factorization and this factorization is unique (Fundamental Theorem of Arithmetic).

- *Name a non-prime factor of 72. What is the prime factorization of that non-prime factor? Is it contained in 2 × 2 × 2 × 3 × 3, the prime factorization of 72?*

Circle it in the prime factorization.

- *Using the prime factorization of 72, how can we determine the factor that pairs with your number to equal 72?*

Make sure students see that the prime factorization is composed of the prime factorization of both factors.

- *What will the prime factorization of a multiple of 72 have in common with the prime factorization of 72?*

Make sure students see that *every* multiple of 72 will entirely contain the prime factorization of 72.

Materials
- Student notebooks

ACE Assignment Guide for Problem 4.2

Differentiated Instruction
Solutions for All Learners

Core 4–7, 12, 13, 14, 27–29
Other *Applications* 8–11, 15–18; *Connections* 30; *Extensions* 35; unassigned choices from previous problems

Adapted For suggestions about adapting ACE problems, see the CMP *Special Needs Handbook*.

Answers to Problem 4.2

A. From our pictures, we can read that
100 = 2 × 2 × 5 × 5, a factorization of the number 100 into prime numbers. From Problem 4.1, we know this factorization is unique, so we call it *the* factorization instead of *a* factorization.

B. 72 = 2 × 2 × 2 × 3 × 3
120 = 2 × 2 × 2 × 3 × 5
600 = 2 × 2 × 2 × 3 × 5 × 5

C. $72 = 2^3 \times 3^2$
$120 = 2^3 \times 3 \times 5$
$600 = 2^3 \times 3 \times 5^2$

D. 1. A student might pick the factor 9, for example. She might write out the factorization of 72 and circle 3 × 3.

72 = 3 × 3 × 2 × 2 × 2

2. She might circle the other factors to exhibit the factor 8.

72 = 3 × 3 × 2 × 2 × 2

Make sure the students see that the entire prime factorization of 72 is composed of the prime factorization of 9 and the prime factorization of 8.

E. If a student picks 144, she can write out the factorization of 72 and show that the prime factorization of 144 is only different by a factor of 2. Make sure the student sees that *every* multiple of 72 will have a prime factorization that entirely contains the prime factorization of 72.

4.3 Using Prime Factorizations

Goals

- Understand that prime numbers are the essential multiplicative building blocks for whole numbers

- Find common factors, greatest common factors, common multiples, and least common multiples using prime factorizations

In this section, students will notice that the Fundamental Theorem of Arithmetic can be used to find the least common multiple and greatest common factor, and they will use prime factorization to develop a straightforward way to find the LCM or GCF.

Students have looked at finding common multiples and common factors of pairs of numbers in Investigation 2.3, using Venn diagrams to show the relationships. But this method is not especially efficient. Using prime factorizations is an efficient method that always works to find common multiples and factors.

Launch 4.3

Suggested Questions Review with your students the ideas covered thus far in the unit.

- *Earlier in this unit, we learned about common factors and common multiples of two numbers. Let's revisit those ideas.*

- *What are the common factors of 24 and 60?*

- *What are the common multiples of 24 and 60?*

Allow students to use various strategies. Students may use lists or Venn diagrams like they did in Investigation 2. Some may try to use the prime factorizations. This is where we are heading. It is okay if students do not think to use the prime factorizations at this time. We will introduce the idea soon. After students have a few minutes to work, have them share their results and their strategies.

- *What are the prime factorizations of 24 and 60?*

Write them in a visible place—on the blackboard, for example.

$$24 = 2 \times 2 \times 2 \times 3$$
$$60 = 2 \times 2 \times 3 \times 5$$

Remind students of the Venn diagrams they did in Problem 2.3 by putting up the Venn diagram transparency of common factors for 24 and 60.

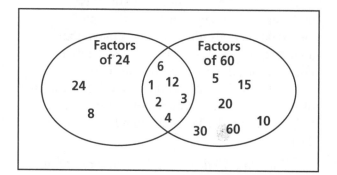

It is important to note that we do not want the focus of this problem to be on Venn diagrams. On the contrary, we are hoping that students will see how efficient prime factorizations are for solving the same kinds of problems addressed earlier with Venn diagrams.

- *Here we have a Venn diagram like the ones we used in Problem 2.3 to find common factors of two numbers. Let's pick a common factor of 24 and 60.*

Pick the factor 12. Ask a student to write the prime factorization of 12 on the board near the factorizations of 24 and 60.

- *What does the factorization of 12 have in common with the factorizations of 24 and 60? (Push students to see that the prime factorization of 12 is a "substring" of the prime factorizations of both 24 and 60.)*

- *Let's pick another common factor of 24 and 60.*

This time, say you look at 6. Have a student write up the prime factorization of 6, noticing that 3 × 2 is a substring of the prime factorizations of 24 and 60.

- *Can we make any conjectures about the prime factorization of any common factor of 24 and 60? (The students should conjecture that the prime factorizations of common factors are "substrings" of the factorizations of both 24 and 60.)*

- *What is the LONGEST factor string that 24 and 60 have in common? (2 × 2 × 3)*

- *And we know that 2 × 2 × 3 = 12 is a common factor of 24 and 60. Can we find a greater common factor? Why or why not?* (We cannot, because any common factor would have to have a prime factorization entirely contained in the prime factorizations of both 24 and 60.)

CAUTION! Make sure your students understand that having a "longer" prime factorization does not necessarily mean that a number is "greater" than another number. For example, the prime factorization of 32 is 2 × 2 × 2 × 2 × 2, and the prime factorization of 49 is 7 × 7, but of course 49 is greater than 32.

Now put up the Venn diagram for multiples of 24 and 60.

- *For some kinds of problems, we need to find common factors. For others we need to find common multiples. Let's think about common multiples and see whether we can find a way to use prime factorizations to help us find them. What are the common multiples of 24 and 60?*

Here the conversation can proceed looking at whether prime factorizations help us find common multiples—and in particular the least common multiple of 24 and 60. Since these ideas are less obvious to students, you may need to just raise questions for them to think about and use more of the following discussion for a summary after the students have a chance to work on the problem.

Suggested Questions Here are questions that can guide the students' thinking:

- *If we find the product of two numbers, for example 24 × 60, will the product be a common multiple? If so, why?*

Write the prime factorization of the product of 24 × 60: 2 × 2 × 2 × 3 × 2 × 2 × 3 × 5.

- *Is this product a multiple of both 24 and 60? How do you know?*

- *If so, what do you multiply 24 by to get 2 × 2 × 2 × 3 × 2 × 2 × 3 × 5?* (Multiply by 2 × 2 × 3 × 5, or 60.)

- *What do you multiply 60 by to get 2 × 2 × 2 × 3 × 2 × 2 × 3 × 5?* (Multiply 60 by 2 × 2 × 2 × 3, or 24.)

- *This means that both 24 and 60 "live" in the product of the two numbers. Can you circle prime factors from the product that will give you 24?* (Yes. Circle 2 × 2 × 2 × 3.)

- *What about 60?* (Yes. Circle 2 × 2 × 3 × 5.)

- *Let's use these ideas to explore the questions in Problem 4.3.*

Let students work in pairs.

Explore 4.3

Keep in mind that students can use any method they choose to find prime factorizations.

You may need to use some of the questions from the launch for those students who still need help.

Summarize 4.3

Suggested Questions The questions in the launch can be used again in the summary. The answers that students have for the questions should be qualitatively better than during the launch.

- *Let's look at 72 and 120. What can you say that is always true about the prime factorization of the common factors for two (or more) numbers? Use 72 and 120 as your example.* (The prime factorization of a common factor of two or more numbers will be contained in the prime factorization of each of the numbers.)

- *Describe a strategy that makes sense to you to find the greatest factor that two or more numbers have in common.* (Ask more than one student to share their thinking. Be sure that finding prime factorizations and forming a number from the greatest overlap of prime factors is one of the strategies given. If students seem to prefer listing all the factors of each number, give a pair of large numbers, for example 2,520 and 2,700, and ask for the greatest common factor. The prime factorizations are 2,520 = 2 × 2 × 2 × 3 × 3 × 5 × 7 and 2,700 = 2 × 2 × 3 × 3 × 3 × 5 × 5. So the overlap is 2 × 2 × 3 × 3 × 5 = 180. If you listed all the factors of 2,520 and 2,700, there would be 48 for 2,520 and 36 for 2,700. This is quite a chore!!)

- *What can we say about multiples of 2 or more numbers? To explore this question, let's list some multiples of 24 that are also multiples of 60.* (120, 240, 360, etc.)

- *What will be true of the factorization of any common multiple of 24 and 60?* (The prime factorization of the least common multiple, 120, is $2 \times 2 \times 2 \times 3 \times 5$. Any greater common multiple will contain the prime factorization of 120, the least common multiple.)

- *Now let's describe some strategies for finding the least common multiple for 72 and 120.* (Call on students to give their strategies. Be sure that using prime factorizations is one strategy considered. $72 = 2 \times 2 \times 2 \times 3 \times 3$ and $120 = 2 \times 2 \times 2 \times 3 \times 5$. To be a common multiple, a number must contain the factorizations of both numbers. We can construct the needed common multiple by starting with the prime factorization of 72, $2 \times 2 \times 2 \times 3 \times 3$, and multiplying this prime factorization by the factors needed to be sure 120 is represented in the string of primes. We have the three 2's and the 3 that we need, but we do not have the factor 5. So we multiply by 5, $2 \times 2 \times 2 \times 3 \times 3 \times 5$, and the number we produce, $2 \times 2 \times 2 \times 3 \times 3 \times 5 = 360$, will contain each prime factor of both 72 and 120 and will be a common multiple.)

- *How can you check to make sure 360 is a common multiple of 72 and 120?* (Divide 360 by each of 72 and 120 to see that 360 is a multiple.)

- *Could a lesser number work?* (No. We constructed the least number that will work. Since $360 \div 72 = 5$, we see that 5 is the extra factor that we needed to make sure 120 was contained in the number 360. The prime factorization of 120 is shown with the factor 5 underlined: $2 \times 2 \times 2 \times 3 \times 3 \times \underline{5}$. Since $360 \div 120 = 3$, we see that the extra 3 in the factorization of 72 is the multiplier. The prime factorization of 72 is shown with the factor 3 not needed for 120 underlined: $2 \times 2 \times 2 \times 3 \times \underline{3} \times 5$. No lesser number will work.)

- *List five more common multiples of 72 and 120 and tell how they relate to the least common multiple.* (Each common multiple is a multiple of the least common multiple.)

There are many other questions that can help students see the power of prime factorizations. For example:

- *Is 24 a factor of 60?* (No.)

- *How can you use the prime factorizations of 24 and 60 to see that 24 is not a factor of 60?* (The prime factorization of 60, $2 \times 2 \times 3 \times 5$, does not contain all of the prime factorization of 24, $2 \times 2 \times 2 \times 3$. You would need another factor of "2" to have 24 contained in 60.)

- *How do you know that 14 is not a factor of either 24 or 60?* (We can see that 24 has $2 \times 2 \times 2 \times 3$ in its prime factorization, and 60 has $2 \times 2 \times 3 \times 5$. We know that $14 = 7 \times 2$, but 7 is not a factor of 24 or 60. Therefore, 14 cannot be a factor of 24 or 60.)

- *When you know the prime factorization of a number such as 60, you have all the building blocks that can be used to make all the factors of 60 that are greater than 1. Since $60 = 2 \times 2 \times 3 \times 5$, every factor of 60 except 1 will have a subset of these primes as its prime factorization. So we can have 2, 3, 4, 5, 6, 10, 12, 15, 20, 30, 60 and, of course, 1 as factors.*

For Questions D and E, you could revisit the table suggested in the Teacher's Guide of Problem 3.4. This is not essential, however. The important idea to take from Question D is that numbers with common factors other than 1 have least common multiples that are less than the product of the numbers. The preceding discussion of prime factorizations can help students understand why there is such a relationship between the common factors and the common multiples of two numbers.

4.3 Using Prime Factorizations

Mathematical Goals

- Understand that prime numbers are the essential multiplicative building blocks for whole numbers
- Find common factors, greatest common factors, common multiples, and least common multiples using prime factorizations

Launch

- *What are the common factors of 24 and 60? The common multiples?*

After students have worked for a few minutes, have them share results and various strategies.

- *What are the prime factorizations of 24 and 60?* Record these.
- *Let's look at 12, a common factor of 24 and 60.*

Write the prime factorization of 12 near those of 24 and 60.

- *What does the factorization of 12 have in common with the others?*

Push students to see that the prime factorization of 12 is a "substring" of those of both 24 and 60. Repeat this with another common factor.

- *Any conjectures about the prime factorization of any common factor?*
- *What is the LONGEST factor string that 24 and 60 have in common?*

Now put up the Venn diagram for multiples of 24 and 60.

- *Let's think about common multiples and see if prime factorizations can help us find them. What are the common multiples of 24 and 60?*

These less obvious ideas might raise questions. Discuss them in summary.

Let students work in pairs.

Materials
- Transparency 4.3

Explore

Allow students to use any method they choose to find prime factorizations. You may need to continue asking questions for those who still need help.

Summarize

- *Let's look at 72 and 120. What is always true about the prime factorization of the common factors of two (or more) numbers?*
- *Describe a strategy to find the greatest common factor of two numbers.*

If students seem to prefer listing all the factors of each number instead of looking at the greatest overlap of prime factors, ask:

- *What is the greatest common factor of 2,520 and 2,700?*
- *What is true of the factorization of* any *common multiple of 24 and 60?*
- *Describe strategies for finding the least common multiple of 72 and 120.*

Be sure that using prime factorizations is one strategy that is discussed.

- *How can you check if 360 is a common multiple of 72 and 120?*

Materials
- Student notebooks

Optional Vocabulary
- relatively prime

continued on next page

- *Could a lesser number work? List five more common multiples of 72 and 120 and tell how they relate to the least common multiple.*

For Questions D and E, focus on prime factorizations to help answer the questions. Help students see the power of prime factorizations.

- *Use the prime factorizations of 24 and 60 to show 24 is not a factor of 60.*
- *How do you know that 14 is not a factor of either 24 or 60?*
- *With the prime factorization of a number, you have all the building blocks to make all the factors greater than 1. Since 60 = 2 × 2 × 3 × 5, each factor of 60, other than 1, will have a subset of these primes as its prime factorization: 2, 3, 4, 5, 6, 10, 12, 15, 20, 30, and 60.*

ACE Assignment Guide for Problem 4.3

Core 19–22, 32
Other *Applications* 23, 24; *Connections* 33; *Extensions* 36; unassigned choices from previous problems

Adapted For suggestions about adapting ACE exercises, see the CMP *Special Needs Handbook*.

Answers to Problem 4.3

A. 1. $72 = 2 \times 2 \times 2 \times 3 \times 3$.
$120 = 2 \times 2 \times 2 \times 3 \times 5$. The longest factor string they have in common is $2 \times 2 \times 2 \times 3$.

2. The greatest common factor is $2 \times 2 \times 2 \times 3 = 24$. There cannot be a greater common factor, because that common factor would have to have a prime factorization that is totally included in the prime factorizations of both 72 and 120.

B. 1. $2 \times 2 \times 2 \times 3 \times 3 \times 5 = 360$. This is the least common multiple of 72 and 120. If the factor string were made shorter by removing a prime factor, the product would no longer be a multiple of at least one of the numbers.

2. We cannot find a "greatest" common multiple of 72 and 120, because we can multiply any common multiple of 72 and 120 by 2 (for example) and get a "greater" common multiple.

C. $12 = 2 \times 2 \times 3$ and $25 = 5 \times 5$. Since 12 and 25 have no common prime factors, they are relatively prime. Another relatively prime pair is 16 and 9.

D. 1. Possible answers: 5 and 4; 8 and 63. If the prime factorizations have no factors in common, the least common multiple of the two numbers will be the product of the numbers. For example, you may want to point out that the least common multiple of two distinct prime numbers is always the product of the two numbers. Of course, it is not always true that the least common multiple of two composite numbers is less than the product. You might push the students to make generalizations. Students should be able to find many examples.

2. Possible answers: 8 and 40; 10 and 15. The least common multiple of two numbers will be less than the product of the numbers whenever the numbers have factors in common.

3. The least common multiple of two numbers will be less than the product of the numbers whenever the numbers have factors, or primes, in common.

E. The greatest common factor of 12 and 16 is 4. The least common multiple of 12 and 16 is 48. $4 \times 48 = 192 = 12 \times 16$. This works for any two numbers. You can see why if you write down the prime factorizations of the numbers.

Investigation 4

Factorizations: Searching for Factor Strings

Some numbers can be written as the product of several different pairs of factors. For example, 100 can be written as 1×100, 2×50, 4×25, 5×20, and 10×10. It is also possible to write 100 as the product of three factors, such as $2 \times 2 \times 25$ and $2 \times 5 \times 10$.

Getting Ready for Problem 4.1

Can you find a longer string of factors with a product of 100?

4.1 The Product Puzzle

The Product Puzzle is a number-search puzzle in which you look for strings of factors with a product of 840. Two factor strings have been marked in the puzzle at the right.

How many factor strings can you find?

The Product Puzzle

5	42	14	15	56	3
20	3	4	420	28	5
70	12	35	210	2	168
120	24	14	2	28	84
7	280	3	4	6	10
3	2	105	140	4	5
20	40	8	21	2	7

Notes _____

_____

_____

_____

In the Product Puzzle, find as many factor strings for 840 as you can. When you find a string, draw a line through it. Keep a list of the strings you find.

A. What is the longest factor string you found?

B. If possible, name a factor string with a product of 840 that is longer than any string you found in the puzzle. Do not consider strings that contain 1.

C. Choose a factor string with two factors. How can you use this string to find a factor string with three factors?

D. How do you know when you have found the longest possible string of factors for a number?

E. How many distinct longest strings of factors are there for 840? Strings are *distinct* if they are different in some way other than the order in which the factors are listed.

The Product Puzzle

5	42	14	15	56	3
20	3	4	420	28	5
70	12	35	210	2	168
120	24	14	2	28	84
7	280	3	4	6	10
3	2	105	140	4	5
20	40	8	21	2	7

ACE Homework starts on page 56.

4.2 Finding the Longest Factor String

The strings of factors of a number are called **factorizations** of that number. In Problem 4.1, you saw that the longest possible factor string for 840 is made up of prime numbers. We call this string the **prime factorization** of 840. In fact, the longest factor string for any whole number is the prime factorization. Can you explain why?

Getting Ready for Problem 4.2

When you look for the prime factorization of a number, it helps to have a list of prime numbers handy. Look back at the table of first moves you made for the Factor Game. Make a list of all prime numbers less than 30.

Notes _____

_____

_____

_____

Derrick wanted to find the common factors and common multiples of 24 and 60. He made Venn diagrams similar to the ones you made in Problem 2.3. He conjectured that he could use prime factorization to find common factors.

First, he found the prime factorizations of 24 and 60.

$$24 = 2 \times 2 \times 2 \times 3$$
$$60 = 2 \times 2 \times 3 \times 5$$

Both prime factorizations contain 2×2, which shows that 4 is a common factor.

$$24 = \boxed{2 \times 2} \times 2 \times 3$$
$$60 = \boxed{2 \times 2} \times 3 \times 5$$

Both prime factorizations contain 2×3, which shows that 6 is a common factor.

$$24 = 2 \times 2 \times \boxed{2 \times 3}$$
$$60 = 2 \times \boxed{2 \times 3} \times 5$$

Derrick noticed that the longest string common to both factorizations is $2 \times 2 \times 3$, so 12 must be the greatest common factor. He then checked a Venn Diagram and found that he was right.

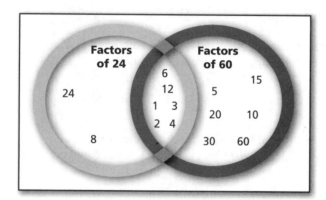

STUDENT PAGE

STUDENT PAGE

Notes _____

_____

_____

_____

(53) 92

Derrick wondered if he could use a similar method to find the least common multiple. He realized that the prime factorization of any multiple of 24 will include its prime factorization, $2 \times 2 \times 2 \times 3$. The prime factorization of any multiple of 60 will contain its prime factorization, $2 \times 2 \times 3 \times 5$.

So, Derrick thought the prime factorization of any common multiple should include $2 \times 2 \times 2 \times 3 \times 5$. Is he right? Check this on the Venn diagram below:

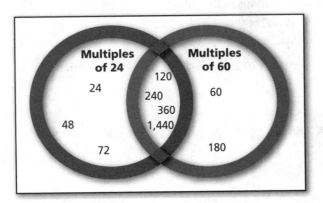

Problem 4.3 Using Prime Factorizations

A. 1. Write the prime factorizations of 72 and 120 that you found in Problem 4.2. What is the longest string common to both factorizations?

2. What is the greatest common factor of 72 and 120? How do you know?

B. 1. What is the shortest string of factors that includes the prime factorizations of both 72 and 120? Can you find a smaller common multiple of 72 and 120? Why or why not?

2. Can you find a greatest common multiple of 72 and 120? Why or why not?

C. Numbers whose greatest common factor is 1, such as 25 and 12, are **relatively prime.** How can you determine that 25 and 12 are relatively prime by looking at their prime factorizations? Find another pair of relatively prime numbers.

Notes _____

_____

_____

_____

D. 1. Find two pairs of numbers whose least common multiple is the product of the numbers. For example, $5 \times 6 = 30$, and the least common multiple of 5 and 6 is 30.

2. Find two pairs of numbers whose least common multiple is less than the product of the numbers. For example, $6 \times 8 = 48$, but the least common multiple of 6 and 8 is 24.

3. How can you determine from the prime factorizations whether the least common multiple of two numbers is the product of the numbers or is less than the product of the two numbers? Explain your thinking.

E. If you multiply the greatest common factor of 12 and 16 by the least common multiple of 12 and 16, you get 192, which is equal to 12×16. Does this work for any two numbers? Why or why not?

ACE **Homework starts on page 56.**

Did You Know?

In all mathematics, there are a few relationships that are so basic that they are called *fundamental theorems*. There is the Fundamental Theorem of Calculus, the Fundamental Theorem of Algebra, and you have found the Fundamental Theorem of Arithmetic. The Fundamental Theorem of Arithmetic states that every whole number greater than one has exactly *one* prime factorization (except for the order in which the factors are written).

Go Online
PHSchool.com   **For:** Information about fundamental theorems
Web Code: ame-9031

STUDENT PAGE

Notes _____

_____

_____

_____

Applications

To solve a multiplication maze, you must find a path of numbers from the entrance to the exit so that the product of the numbers in the path equals the puzzle number. No diagonal moves are allowed. Below is the solution of a multiplication maze for 840.

Multiplication Maze 840

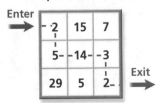

Solve each multiplication maze. **Hint:** It may help to find the longest factor string of the puzzle number.

1. **Multiplication Maze 840**

2. **Multiplication Maze 360**

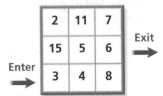

3. Make a multiplication maze for 720. Be sure to record your solution.

For Exercises 4–11, find the prime factorization of each number.

4. 36   **5.** 180   **6.** 525   **7.** 165

8. 293   **9.** 760   **10.** 216   **11.** 231

12. Use exponents to rewrite the prime factorizations you found in Exercises 4–11.

13. To indicate multiplication, you can use a raised dot symbol. For example, $3 \times 5 = 3 \cdot 5$. Find the prime factorization of 312 using raised dot symbols.

56   Prime Time

Notes _____

_____

_____

_____

14. Multiple Choice What is the prime factorization of 240?

    A. $10 \cdot 24$ **B.** $2 \cdot 3 \cdot 5$

    C. $2^3 \cdot 3 \cdot 5$ **D.** $2^4 \cdot 3 \cdot 5$

15. Jill and Jamahl are comparing their special numbers. Jill's number has a prime factorization with six prime numbers. Jamahl's number has a prime factorization with only three numbers. Jill says this means her number is greater than Jamahl's. Jamahl says that is not necessarily true. Who is right?

16. Find all the numbers less than 100 that have at least one 2 and at least one 5 in their prime factorization. What do you notice about these numbers?

17. Multiple Choice Choose the number that is the product of exactly three different prime numbers.

    F. 15   **G.** 20   **H.** 30   **J.** 57

18. Find all the numbers less than 100 that are the product of exactly three different prime numbers.

Homework Help Online
PHSchool.com
For: Help with Exercise 18
Web Code: ame-1418

For Exercises 19–24, find the greatest common factor and the least common multiple for each pair of numbers.

19. 36 and 45   **20.** 30 and 75   **21.** 78 and 104

22. 15 and 60   **23.** 32 and 45   **24.** 37 and 12

Connections

25. Mr. Rawlings has 60 cookies. He wants to give each of his 16 grandchildren the same number of cookies for a snack. What is the greatest number of cookies he can give each child? After he gives his grandchildren their cookies, how many cookies will he have left for himself?

26. Mr. and Mrs. Fisk have 8 children. Each of those children has 8 children. How many grandchildren do Mr. and Mrs. Fisk have? If each grandchild has 8 children, how many great-grandchildren do Mr. and Mrs. Fisk have?

Investigation 4 Factorizations: Searching for Factor Strings   **57**

Notes

27. Rosa claims the longest string of prime factors for 30 is 2 × 3 × 5. Tyee claims there is a longer string, 1 × 2 × 1 × 3 × 1 × 5. Who is correct? Why?

28. The number 1 is not prime. Why do you think mathematicians decided not to call 1 a prime number?

29. a. Find the multiples of 9 that are less than 100.

    b. Find the multiples of 21 that are less than 100.

    c. Find the common multiples of 9 and 21 that are less than 100.

    d. What is the next common multiple of 9 and 21?

Go Online
PHSchool.com
For: Multiple-Choice Skills Practice
Web Code: ama-1454

30. For each part below, use your birth year or the birth year of one of your family members as your number.

    a. Find the prime factorization of your number.

    b. Describe your number to a friend, giving your friend as much information as you can about the number. Here are some ideas to include: Is the number square, prime, even, or odd? How many factors does it have? Is it a multiple of some other number?

31. Tomas and Sharlina work on weekends and holidays doing odd jobs around the neighborhood. They are paid by the day, not the hour. They each earn the same whole number of dollars per day. Last month Tomas earned $184 and Sharlina earned $207. How many days did each person work? What is their daily pay?

32. What is my number?

    Clue 1 My number is a multiple of 2 and 7.

    Clue 2 My number is less than 100 but greater than 50.

    Clue 3 My number is the product of three different prime numbers.

33. What is my number?

    Clue 1 My number is a perfect square.

    Clue 2 The only prime number in its prime factorization is 2.

    Clue 3 My number is a factor of 32.

    Clue 4 The sum of its digits is odd.

Notes _____

_____

_____

_____

Extensions

34. Most years contain 365 days, but certain years, called *leap years*, contain 366 days. Leap years occur in years divisible by four, with some exceptions. Years divisible by 100 are *not* leap years—unless they are divisible by 400. So 1896 was a leap year, but 1900 wasn't. Both 1996 and 2000 were leap years. A week has 7 days.

    a. How many weeks are in each type of year?

    b. January 1, 2004, fell on a Thursday. On what dates did the next three Thursdays of 2004 occur?

    c. The year 2004 was a leap year. It had 366 days. What day of the week was January 1, 2005?

    d. What is the pattern, over several years, for the days on which your birthday will fall?

35. The Fundamental Theorem of Arithmetic was first stated by the Greek mathematician Euclid. He wrote: "If a number is the least that is measured by prime numbers, it will not be measured by any prime except those originally measuring it." After studying prime factorizations in this Investigation, what do you suppose Euclid meant?

36. Mr. Barkley has a box of books. He says the number of books in the box is divisible by 2, 3, 4, 5, and 6. How many books could be in the box? Add another factor so that there is only one possible solution.

Did You Know?

If you were born on any day other than February 29, leap day, it takes at least 5 years for your birthday to come around to the same day of the week. It follows a pattern of 5 years, then 6 years, then 11 years, and then 6 years (or some variation of that pattern), to fall on the same day of the week. If you were born on February 29, it takes 28 years for your birthday to fall on the same day of the week!

Mathematical Reflections 4

In this investigation, you found factor strings for numbers, and you saw how the prime factorizations of numbers could be used to find common factors and multiples. These questions will help you summarize what you have learned.

Think about your answers to these questions. Discuss your ideas with other students and your teacher. Then write a summary of your findings in your notebook.

1. **a.** Does every number have a prime factorization?

   b. How many prime factorizations does a number have?

   c. Why is it important that 1 is not a prime number?

2. **a.** How can you use the prime factorization of two numbers to find their least common multiple? Give examples.

   b. How can you use the prime factorization of two numbers to find their greatest common factor? Give examples.

   c. How can you use the prime factorization of two numbers to determine whether they are relatively prime? Give examples.

3. If you know the greatest common factor of two numbers is 1, can you predict what the least common multiple will be?

Unit Project What's Next?

Don't forget your special number! What is its prime factorization?

Notes _____

_____

_____

_____

Investigation 4

ACE Assignment Choices

Differentiated Instruction
Solutions for All Learners

Problem 4.1
Core 1–3, 25
Other *Connections* 26, *Extensions* 34

Problem 4.2
Core 4–7, 12, 13, 14, 27–29
Other *Applications* 8–11, 15–18; *Connections* 30; *Extensions* 35; unassigned choices from previous problems

Problem 4.3
Core 19–22, 32
Other *Applications* 23, 24; *Connections* 33; *Extensions* 36; unassigned choices from previous problems

Adapted For suggestions about adapting Exercises 1–3 and other ACE exercises, see the CMP *Special Needs Handbook*.

Applications

1. The path is $7 \times 5 \times 2 \times 3 \times 4$.

2. The path is $3 \times 4 \times 5 \times 6$.

3. Puzzles will vary.

4. $2 \times 2 \times 3 \times 3$

5. $2 \times 2 \times 3 \times 3 \times 5$

6. $3 \times 5 \times 5 \times 7$

7. $3 \times 5 \times 11$

8. 293

9. $2 \times 2 \times 2 \times 5 \times 19$

10. $2 \times 2 \times 2 \times 3 \times 3 \times 3$

11. $3 \times 7 \times 11$

12. $36 = 2^2 \times 3^2$, $180 = 2^2 \times 3^2 \times 5$, $525 = 3 \times 5^2 \times 7$, $165 = 3 \times 5 \times 11$, $293 = 293$, $760 = 2^3 \times 5 \times 19$, $216 = 2^3 \times 3^3$, and $231 = 3 \times 7 \times 11$

13. $2 \cdot 2 \cdot 2 \cdot 3 \cdot 13$

14. D

15. Jamahl is correct. Possible answer: Consider 216. It has six prime factors: $2 \times 2 \times 2 \times 3 \times 3 \times 3$. Then consider 231. It has three prime factors: $3 \times 7 \times 11$. 231 is greater than 216, even though it has fewer prime factors.

16. 10, 20, 30, 40, 50, 60, 70, 80, and 90. The numbers are the multiples of 10 (2×5) less than 100.

17. H

18. $2 \times 3 \times 5 = 30$, $2 \times 3 \times 7 = 42$, $2 \times 3 \times 11 = 66$, $2 \times 3 \times 13 = 78$, $2 \times 5 \times 7 = 70$

19. GCF = 9, LCM = 180

20. GCF = 15, LCM = 150

21. GCF = 26, LCM = 312

22. GCF = 15, LCM = 60

23. GCF = 1, LCM = 1,440

24. GCF = 1, LCM = 444

Connections

25. He can give each child 3 cookies, and he will have 12 left for himself.

26. $8 \times 8 = 64$, so they have 64 grandchildren. They have 512 great-grandchildren.

27. Rosa is correct because the number 1 is not a prime number. Tyee is correct that his string is a longer string of factors, but it is not a string of prime factors for 30.

28. Mathematicians have determined that it is important for a number to be able to be identified by its longest string of factors. If the number 1 were prime, the prime factorization for a number would have to include 1, and *could* include 1 as a factor any number of times. So a prime factorization would not be the same as the longest string possible without using 1.

29. a. 9, 18, 27, 36, 45, 54, 63, 72, 81, 90, and 99

b. 21, 42, 63, and 84

c. 63

d. 126

30. a. Possible answers: $1994 = 2 \times 997$,
$1995 = 3 \times 5 \times 7 \times 19$,
$1996 = 2 \times 2 \times 499, 1997 = 1997$,
$1998 = 2 \times 3 \times 3 \times 3 \times 37, 1999 = 1999$,
$2000 = 2 \times 2 \times 2 \times 2 \times 5 \times 5 \times 5$.

b. Answers will vary. For example, 1996 is not square; it is a multiple of 4 and of 998. It is not prime, and it is even.

31. Factor to find that $184 = 8 \times 23$ and $207 = 9 \times 23$. 23 is the only common factor other than 1. Therefore Tomas worked 8 days at $23 per day and Sharina worked 9 days at $23 per day.

32. Since the number is a multiple of 2 and 7 (Clue 1), it must be a multiple of 14. The multiples of 14 between 50 and 100 (Clue 2) are

$56 = 2 \times 2 \times 2 \times 7$,
$70 = 2 \times 5 \times 7$,
$84 = 2 \times 2 \times 3 \times 7$, and
$98 = 2 \times 7 \times 7$.

Of these numbers, only 70 is the product of three different prime numbers (Clue 3). The number is 70.

33. The factors of 32 are 1, 2, 4, 8, 16, and 32 (Clue 3). Of these numbers, only 1, 16, and 32 have digits that add to odd numbers (Clue 4). 1 and 16 are square numbers (Clue 1). Of these two numbers, only 16 has 2 in its prime factorization (Clue 2). The number is 16.

Extensions

34. a. 52 weeks, with 1 extra day if it is not a leap year and 2 extra days if it is a leap year.

b. January 8, 15, and 22

c. Saturday

d. Your birthday will fall one day later in the week each year, except when leap day (February 29) falls between your birthdays. In that case, your birthday will be two days later in the week. If your birthday is February 29, your birthday will be five days later in the week every time it occurs.

35. Answers will vary. Sample: If a number is the least common multiple of several prime numbers, its prime factorization will contain only those primes, and no others.

36. The common multiples of 2, 3, 4, 5, and 6 are 60, 120, 180, ... If we add the clue that the box contains fewer than 100 books, the only answer would be 60.

Possible Answers to Mathematical Reflections

1. a. Every number (greater than 1) has a prime factorization.

b. Every number has exactly one prime factorization.

c. 1 cannot be prime because otherwise prime factorizations could not be unique.

2. a. If you write down the prime factorizations of two numbers, the shortest factor string that includes the prime factorizations of both numbers gives the least common multiple of the two numbers. For example, $16 = 2 \times 2 \times 2 \times 2$ and $14 = 2 \times 7$, so the least common multiple of 16 and 14 is $2 \times 2 \times 2 \times 2 \times 7 = 112$.

b. If you write down the prime factorizations of two numbers, the longest factor string the two numbers have in common gives the greatest common factor. For example, $36 = 2 \times 2 \times 3 \times 3$ and $32 = 2 \times 2 \times 2 \times 2 \times 2$. The longest factor string the two factorizations have in common is 2×2, so the greatest common factor of 36 and 32 is 4.

c. Two numbers are relatively prime if they have no factors in common. For example, 125 and 64 are relatively prime because $125 = 5 \times 5 \times 5$ and $64 = 2 \times 2 \times 2 \times 2 \times 2 \times 2$, so there are no common factors. This means that their only common factor is 1.

3. If you know the greatest common factor of two numbers is 1, then the least common multiple will be the product of the two numbers.

Investigation 5 — Putting It All Together

Mathematical and Problem-Solving Goals

- Use the multiplicative structure of numbers, such as primes, composites, factors, multiples, and square numbers, to reason mathematically and to solve interesting problems

- Simulate a problem, gather data, make conjectures, and create arguments to justify those conjectures

- Communicate one's mathematical ideas clearly

Summary of Problems

Problem 5.1 **Unraveling the Locker Problem**

Students use many of the properties they have learned about numbers to unravel a fanciful problem about a new school with 1,000 lockers. (A very good article by Peggy House on the Locker Problem appeared in the October 1980 issue of *Arithmetic Teacher*.) This investigation serves as a wrap-up to the study of numbers in this unit, but these skills should continue to develop throughout the year as the students work on other problems in other units. If time is short, you could assign this problem as an extra credit, outside-class problem. If done in class, you have the opportunity for a substantive classroom discussion that can help students who have not yet connected all the ideas of the unit to solidify the concepts of factors and multiples and the computational strategies for finding them.

	Suggested Pacing	Materials for Students	Materials for Teachers	ACE Assignments
All	$2\frac{1}{2}$ days	Calculators; colored pens, pencils, or markers; blank transparencies and transparency markers (optional); student notebooks	Blank transparencies and transparency markers	
5.1	2 days	Grid paper to help simulate the first problem, two color chips or other similar manipulatives, Labsheets 5.1A and 5.1B (12 total, copied front-to-back, optional)	Transparencies 5.1 and 5ACE Exercise 25	1–25
MR	$\frac{1}{2}$ day			

header/section title block
5.1 Unraveling the Locker Problem

Goals

- Use the multiplicative structure of numbers, such as primes, composites, factors, multiples, and square numbers, to reason mathematically and to solve interesting problems

- Simulate a problem, gather data, make conjectures, and create arguments to justify those conjectures

- Communicate one's mathematical ideas clearly

This section serves as a summary for the unit. All the ideas of the unit can be revisited through this section.

Launch 5.1

To help students understand the context of the problem, many teachers use students to simulate what happens to the first few doors of the lockers. Here is a way that some teachers have launched the problem. They make 12 signs with an open door on one side and a closed door on the other side and number the doors 1 to 12. (You can use pieces of paper with "open" written on one side and "closed" written on the other. It helps to write the locker number on both sides. Or you can use Labsheets 5.1A and 5.1B.)

Twelve students are selected to play the role of locker doors (to hold the signs). Twelve other students will play the role of students 1 to 12 in the new school. The students who are playing the role of lockers will hold up a door sign and turn it over each time their locker is touched by a student. The following diagram illustrates what

the lockers would look like after 12 students have taken a turn.

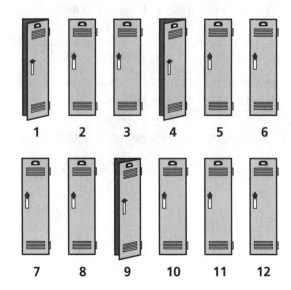

Other teachers help students understand the problem, but do not suggest a way to tackle it, leaving this for the groups of students to decide upon. One problem-solving strategy that works well with this problem is to solve an easier (smaller) problem and then find a pattern.

If the students are having trouble seeing what is happening, a record could be kept, on a chart something like the one in Figure 1 on the next page, to show what happens as the students touch the locker doors.

As students work on the problem, have them consider this question in the Getting Ready:

- *When all the students have finished, which locker doors are open?* (The lockers with square numbers. At this point, students may not be able to answer the question but will be asked the question again in Question B.)

Groups of two to four students work well.

Explore 5.1

Suggested Questions If a group is having any difficulty, suggest that they focus on Question A and simulate the problem for the first 30 (or even 50) lockers. Ask questions such as:

- *How many students will touch Locker 1? Who touches it?*
- *How many students will touch Locker 2? Who touches it?*
- *How many students will touch Locker 3? Who touches it?*
- *Who will touch Locker 25?*
- *How can you explain who will touch any locker?*
- *The first student through changes every single locker. Will anyone else touch every locker?*
- *Which lockers does the second student change? The third student?*
- *If I am the 23rd student, which lockers will I change?*
- *How is the student number related to the lockers that student will change?*

As you circulate, ask for justification. You might use questions such as:

- *Why do you think your answer is correct?*
- *Explain your strategy. Give me an example.*

Summarize 5.1

As you discuss the problem, ask the students to translate the questions from the language of lockers to the language of mathematics and vice versa, from mathematics to lockers. Making this connection between the concrete setting of lockers and the mathematics underpinning the questions is very important. Students need to make this connection very explicit. An example would be Question G. The language of lockers asks, "Which of the students touched both Locker 24 and Locker 36?" In mathematical language the question would be, "What are the common factors of 24 and 36?" After your students have some success in moving between these two representations of the problems, give them a chance to write other pairs of questions—Mathematical and Locker—that can be answered by analyzing the Locker Problem. (See the answers for additional connections between the

Figure 1

Locker #	1	2	3	4	5	6	7	8	9	10	11	12
Custodian	—	—	—	—	—	—	—	—	—	—	—	—
Student # 1	✓	✓	✓	✓	✓	✓	✓	✓	✓	✓	✓	✓
2	✓	—	✓	—	✓	—	✓	—	✓	—	✓	—
3	✓	—	—	—	✓	✓	✓	—	—	—	✓	✓
4	✓	—	—	✓	✓	✓	✓	✓	—	—	✓	—
5	✓	—	—	✓	—	✓	✓	✓	—	✓	✓	—
6	✓	—	—	—	—	✓	✓	✓	—	—	✓	✓
7	✓	—	—	—	—	—	—	✓	✓	✓	✓	✓
8	✓	—	—	—	—	—	—	—	✓	✓	✓	✓
9	✓	—	—	—	—	—	—	—	✓	—	✓	✓
10	✓	—	—	—	—	—	—	—	✓	✓	✓	✓
11	✓	—	—	—	—	—	—	✓	—	—	✓	—
12	✓	—	—	✓	—	—	—	—	✓	—	—	—

locker questions and mathematical concepts from this unit. Primes, square numbers, factors, common factors, multiples, and common multiples are just a few concepts that are revisited.)

Suggested Questions Call on different groups to present their answers and reasons.

- *Name some of the lockers that are open. Why do these end up open while others are closed?*

- *How is the student number related to the locker number?*

- *What is special about the lockers that remain open?*

The solution to the problem depends on recognizing that a locker is touched by every student whose number is a factor of the locker's number. For example, Locker 18 is touched by students 1, 2, 3, 6, 9, and 18. For every *pair* of students that touch a locker, the locker door is changed twice. This means that if it was open, it is still open and if it was closed, it is still closed. Since factors occur in pairs, shouldn't all the lockers end up closed? The surprise is that for certain special numbers—the square numbers—one of their factor pairs consists of two numbers that are the same, for example 2 × 2 for the number 4. This factor pair produces only one distinct factor. Therefore, all the lockers with square numbers will be touched an odd number of times and will end up open. The squares from 1 to 1,000 are: 1, 4, 9, 16, 25, 36, 49, 64, 81, 100, 121, 144, 169, 196, 225, 256, 289, 324, 361, 400, 441, 484, 529, 576, 625, 676, 729, 784, 841, 900, 961. Therefore, only 31 of the 1,000 lockers will end up open.

Additional interesting questions to explore are:

- *Which lockers are touched by exactly two people?*

If they do not say they are primes, ask:

- *What is special about these numbers?* (The locker numbers are primes.)

- *If I choose any locker number, how can you determine who will touch that locker?* (The students whose numbers are factors of the locker numbers will touch the locker.)

- *When you need to know the first locker touched by two students (as in Question E), what are you looking for?* (the least common multiple of the two student numbers)

- *What strategy can you use to find it?*

- *How can you determine the last locker touched by both students?* (It is the greatest common multiple less than 1,000. This only has a greatest common multiple because the lockers stop. There is no greatest common multiple of a number because numbers are infinite.)

- *A student touches two different lockers. What do you know about the student number and the two lockers?* (The student number is a common factor of the two locker numbers, and the locker numbers are multiples of the student number.)

- *Who will be the last student to touch those two lockers?* (The one whose number is the greatest common factor of the locker numbers.)

- *If I give you two locker numbers, what strategy would you use to determine which students touched both?* (Students should discuss a strategy for finding common factors.)

5.1 Unraveling the Locker Problem

Mathematical Goals

- Use the multiplicative structure of numbers, such as primes, composites, factors, multiples, and square numbers, to reason mathematically and to solve interesting problems
- Simulate a problem, gather data, make conjectures, and create arguments to justify those conjectures
- Communicate one's mathematical ideas clearly

Launch

Simulate what happens to the first few doors of the lockers.

If the students are having trouble seeing what is happening, keep a record on a chart to show what happens as the students touch the locker doors. As students work on the problem, have them consider this question:

- *When all the students have finished, which locker doors are open?*

Groups of two to four students work well.

Materials
- Transparency 5.1
- Labsheets 5.1A and 5.1B

Explore

If a group is having difficulty, focus them on Question A and have them simulate the problem for the first 30 lockers. Ask questions such as:

- *How many students will touch Locker 1? Who touches it?*
- *How many students will touch Locker 2? Who? Locker 3? Who?*
- *Who will touch Locker 25?*
- *Can you explain who will touch any locker?*
- *Will anyone touch every single locker? Will anyone else?*
- *Which lockers does the second student change? The third student?*
- *If I am the 23rd student, which lockers will I change?*
- *How is the student number related to the lockers that student will change?*

As you circulate, ask for justification. You might use questions such as:

- *Why do you think your answer is correct?*
- *Explain your strategy. Give me an example.*

Materials
- Calculators

Summarize

Ask the students to translate the questions from the language of lockers to the language of mathematics and vice versa.

Call on different groups to present their answers and reasons.

- *Name some of the lockers that are open. Why do these end up open while others are closed?*
- *How is the student number related to the locker number?*

Materials
- Student notebooks

continued on next page

Summarize
continued

- *What is special about the lockers that remain open?*
- *Which lockers are touched by exactly two people?*
- *If I choose any locker number, how can you determine who will touch that locker?*
- *When you need to know the first locker touched by two students (as in Question E), what are you looking for?*
- *What strategy can you use to find it?*
- *How can you determine the last locker touched by both students?*
- *A student touches two different lockers. What do you know about the student number and the two lockers?*
- *Who will be the last student to touch those two lockers?*
- *If I give you two locker numbers, what strategy would you use to determine which students touched both?*

ACE Assignment Guide for Problem 5.1

Core 1–3, 5, 6, 10, 11, 13–15
Other *Connections* 4, 7–9, 12, 16; *Extensions* 17–25

Adapted For suggestions about adapting Exercise 9 and other ACE exercises, see the CMP *Special Needs Handbook*.

Answers to Problem 5.1

A. Students may see many different patterns. For example, students might notice that prime numbered lockers are closed because they have only two factors.

B. Square-numbered lockers remain open. They have an odd number of factors. Therefore, the final action will be to open the locker. For example, 16 has five factors, 1, 2, 4, 8, 16. The sequence of the door would be O C O C O.

   The complete list of open lockers is: 1, 4, 9, 16, 25, 36, 49, 64, 81, 100, 121, 144, 169, 196, 225, 256, 289, 324, 361, 400, 441, 484, 529, 576, 625, 676, 729, 784, 841, 900, 961.

C. 1. The lockers that have prime numbers, because they have only two factors. The first few of these are 2, 3, 5, 7, 11, 13, 17, 19, 23, and so on.

   2. These are the squares of prime numbers, which are 4, 9, 25, 49, 121, 169, 289, 361, 529, 841, and 961.

3. These are the numbers that are products of two different primes or numbers whose prime factorization is (prime)^3.

   Examples are 6 (2×3), 10 (2×5), 15 (3×5), 8 ($2 \times 2 \times 2$), 27 ($3 \times 3 \times 3$), and so on.

D. By finding the number of factors of the given locker number.

E. 1. Locker 24, because 24 is the least common multiple of 6 and 8.

   2. Locker 60, because the least common multiple of 12 and 30 is 60.

   3. Locker 91, because the least common multiple of 7 and 13 is 91.

   4. Locker 600, because the least common multiple of 100 and 120 is 600.

F. Since each student touches lockers that are multiples of the student's number, you can find the first locker they both touch by finding the *least common multiple*. The *last* locker touched by both students would be the greatest common multiple that is less than 1,000.

G. 1. Students 1, 2, 3, 4, 6, and 12, because these are the common factors of 24 and 36.

   2. The students are 1, 2, 4, 5, 10, and 20 because these are the common factors of 100 and 120.

   3. The students are 1, 3, 7, and 21, because these are the common factors of 42 and 273.

H. Find the common factors of the two numbers.

Investigation 5

Putting It All Together

You have learned many things about factors and multiples of whole numbers. Now you'll have a chance to use what you know to solve an interesting problem.

1.5 Unraveling the Locker Problem

There are 1,000 lockers in a long hall of Westfalls High. In preparation for the beginning of school, the janitor cleans the lockers and paints fresh numbers on the locker doors. The lockers are numbered from 1 to 1,000. When the 1,000 Westfalls High students return from summer vacation, they decide to celebrate the beginning of the school year by working off some energy.

Notes _____

_____

_____

_____

The first student, Student 1, runs down the row of lockers and opens every door.

Student 2 closes the doors of Lockers 2, 4, 6, 8, and so on to the end of the line.

Student 3 *changes the state of* the doors of Lockers 3, 6, 9, 12, and so on to the end of the line. (This means the student opens the door if it is closed and closes the door if it is open.)

Notes _____

_____

_____

_____

Student 4 changes the state of the doors of Lockers 4, 8, 12, 16, and so on.

Student 5 changes the state of every fifth door, Student 6 changes the state of every sixth door, and so on, until all 1,000 students have had a turn.

active math
online
For: Locker Problem Activity
Visit: PHSchool.com
Web Code: amd-1501

Getting Ready for Problem 5.1

Consider this question:

When all the students have finished, which locker doors are open?

Make a conjecture about the answer to this question. Then, describe a strategy you might use to try to find the answer.

Did You Know

A famous mathematician, George Polya, wrote a book titled *How to Solve It* about problem-solving strategies. He suggests that if you can't solve a problem right away, you might first try to solve a related problem or a simplified version of the problem so that you can look for patterns and strategies to help you. He also suggests drawing pictures. Professor Polya solved some very complicated math problems that way!

Go Online
PHSchool.com
For: Information about prime numbers
Web Code: ame-9031

Notes _____

_____

_____

_____

Problem 5.1 Using Multiples and Factors

A. Model the problem for the first 30 students and the first 30 lockers. What patterns do you see as the students put their plan into action?

B. When the 1,000 students are finished, which locker doors are open? Explain why your answer makes sense. What kind of numbers are these?

C. Give the numbers of several lockers that were touched by exactly

    1. two students. What kind of numbers are these?

    2. three students.

    3. four students.

D. How can you determine exactly how many students have touched a given locker?

E. Which was the first locker touched by

    1. both Student 6 and Student 8?

    2. both Student 12 and Student 30?

    3. both Student 7 and Student 13?

    4. both Student 100 and Student 120?

F. Given two student numbers, how can you determine which locker will be the first touched by both students? How can you determine which locker will be the last touched by both students?

G. Which students touched

    1. both Locker 24 and Locker 36?

    2. both Locker 100 and Locker 120?

    3. both Locker 42 and Locker 273?

H. Given two lockers, how can you determine which students touched both?

ACE Homework starts on page 65.

Notes _____

_____

_____

_____

Applications

For Exercises 1–3, refer to Problem 5.1.

1. Give the numbers of several lockers that were touched by exactly five students.

2. Which was the first locker touched by both

   a. Students 3 and 5?

   b. Students 12 and 20?

   c. Students 72 and 84?

   d. Students 210 and 315?

3. Which students touched both

   a. Lockers 13 and 81?

   b. Lockers 140 and 210?

   c. Lockers 165 and 330?

   d. Lockers 196 and 294?

Connections

4. There are 50 lockers, numbered 1 through 50, in a short hall at Phillips Middle School. Mr. Giannetti hid treats for his class in one of the lockers. He gave the class the following clues about the number of the locker where the treats are located.

   Clue 1 The number is even.

   Clue 2 The number is divisible by 3.

   Clue 3 The number is a multiple of Mr. Giannetti's lucky number, 7.

   In which locker are the treats located?

Notes _____

_____

_____

_____

5. How many factors does each of the following numbers have?

   a. 100   **b.** 101   **c.** 102   **d.** 103

6. Write a mathematical story about the number 648. For example, you might describe its factors and its multiples. You might also give some examples of its relationship to other numbers. Use at least five vocabulary words from this unit in your story.

7. What is the least prime number greater than 50?

8. Ivan said that if a number ends in 0, both 2 and 5 are factors of the number. Is he correct? Why or why not?

For: Help with Exercise 8
Web Code: ame-1508

9. What is my number?

   Clue 1   My number is a multiple of 5 and is less than 50.
   Clue 2   My number is a multiple of 3.
   Clue 3   My number has exactly 8 factors.

10. What is my number?

   Clue 1   My number is a multiple of 5, but it does not end in 5.
   Clue 2   The prime factorization of my number is a string of three numbers.
   Clue 3   Two of the numbers in the prime factorization are the same.
   Clue 4   My number is greater than the seventh square number.

11. Now it's your turn! Make up a set of clues for a mystery number. You might want to use your special number as the mystery number. Include as many ideas from this unit as you can. Try out your clues on a classmate.

For Exercises 12 and 13, describe the numbers that have both of the given numbers as factors.

For: Multiple-Choice Skills Practice
Web Code: ama-1554

12. 2 and 3   **13.** 3 and 5

14. **a.** Find all the numbers between 1 and 1,000 that have 2 as their only prime factor.

   b. What is the next number after 1,000 that has 2 as its only prime factor?

66   Prime Time

Notes _____

_____

_____

_____

15. The numbers 2 and 3 are prime, consecutive numbers. Are there other such pairs of *adjacent primes*? Why or why not?

16. Which group of numbers—evens or odds—contains more prime numbers? Why?

Extensions

17. Goldbach's Conjecture is a famous conjecture that has never been proved true or false. The conjecture states that every even number, except 2, can be written as the sum of two prime numbers. For example, 16 can be written as 5 + 11, which are both prime numbers.

  a. Write the first six even numbers greater than 2 as the sum of two prime numbers.

  b. Write 100 as the sum of two primes.

  c. The number 2 is a prime number. Can an even number greater than 4 be written as the sum of two prime numbers if you use 2 as one of the primes? Why or why not?

18. Multiple Choice Choose the number that is divisible by four different prime numbers.

  A. 77   **B.** 105   **C.** 225   **D.** 1,155

19. Find the least number that is divisible by four different prime numbers.

20. Prime numbers that differ by 2, such as 3 and 5, are called *twin primes*. Starting with the twin primes 5 and 7, look carefully at the numbers between twin primes. What do they have in common? Why?

21. Try to discover a method for finding all the factors of a number using its prime factorization. Use your method to find all the factors of 36. Then use your method to find all the factors of 480.

22. Suppose a number has 2 and 6 as factors. What other numbers must be factors of the number? Explain.

23. Suppose a number is a multiple of 12. Of what other numbers is it a multiple? Explain.

Notes _____

_____

_____

_____

24. Suppose 10 and 6 are common factors of two numbers. What other factors must the numbers have in common? Explain.

25. The chart below shows the factor counts for the numbers from 975 to 1,000. Each star stands for one factor. For example, the four stars after 989 indicate that 989 has four factors.

```
  975  ★★★★★★★★★★★★
  976  ★★★★★★★★★★
  977  ★★
  978  ★★★★★★★★
  979  ★★★★
  980  ★★★★★★★★★★★★★★★★★★
  981  ★★★★★★
  982  ★★★★
  983  ★★
  984  ★★★★★★★★★★★★★★★★
  985  ★★★★
  986  ★★★★★★★★
  987  ★★★★★★★★
  988  ★★★★★★★★★★★★
  989  ★★★★
  990  ★★★★★★★★★★★★★★★★★★★★★★★★
  991  ★★
  992  ★★★★★★★★★★★★
  993  ★★★★
  994  ★★★★★★★★
  995  ★★★★
  996  ★★★★★★★★★★★★
  997  ★★
  998  ★★★★
  999  ★★★★★★★★
1,000  ★★★★★★★★★★★★★★★★
```

Boris thinks that numbers that have many factors, such as 975 and 996, must be abundant numbers. (Recall that an *abundant number* is a number whose proper factors have a sum greater than the number.) Is Boris correct? Explain.

Notes _____

_____

_____

_____

Mathematical Reflections 5

Working on the locker problem gave you an opportunity to use what you know about whole numbers, factors, and multiples. These questions will help you summarize what you have learned.

Think about your answers to these questions. Discuss your ideas with other students and your teacher. Then write a summary of your findings in your notebook.

1. What can you say about a number if all you know is that it has an odd number of factors? Justify your answer.

2. Describe how the following ideas were used in solving parts of the Locker Problem:

   a. prime numbers

   b. divisors

   c. multiples

   d. square numbers

   e. least common multiple

   f. greatest common factor

Unit Project What's Next?

Don't forget your special number. What new things can you say about your number?

Notes

Investigation 5

ACE
Assignment Choices

Differentiated Instruction
Solutions for All Learners

Problem 5.1

Core 1–3, 5, 6, 10, 11, 13–15
Other *Connections* 4, 7–9, 12, 16; *Extensions* 17–25

Adapted For suggestions about adapting Exercise 9 and other ACE exercises, see the CMP *Special Needs Handbook*.

Applications

1. 16, 81, 256, and 625 (the numbers that are a prime number to the fourth power)

2. **a.** Locker 15   **b.** Locker 60
   c. Locker 504   **d.** Locker 630

3. **a.** Only Student 1 touched both lockers because the locker numbers are relatively prime.

   b. Students 1, 2, 5, 7, 10, 14, 35, and 70 touched both lockers 140 and 210. These are the common factors.

   c. Students 1, 3, 5, 11, 15, 33, 55, and 165 touched both lockers 165 and 330. These are the common factors.

   d. Students 1, 2, 7, 14, 49, and 98 touched both lockers 196 and 294. These are the common factors.

Connections

4. Only Locker 42 meets all three criteria. A good way to approach the problem is to list all the even numbers 50 or less and then cross out those that fail to meet each of the other criteria. A student might also start by listing just the numbers divisible by 7 and then apply the other two criteria to those.

5. **a.** $100 = 2^2 \times 5^2$ which has nine factors
   b. 101 is prime and has only two factors
   c. $102 = 2 \times 3 \times 17$ which has eight factors
   d. 103 = is prime and has only two factors

6. Variable answers. You might want to have students post some of their stories around the room.

7. 53

8. Yes. Numbers that end in 0 are multiples of 10. Numbers that are multiples of 10 have both 2 and 5 as factors.

9. A number that is a multiple of 3 (Clue 2) and of 5 (Clue 1) must be a multiple of 15. The multiples of 15 that are less than 50 are 15, 30, and 45. Only 30 has 8 factors (Clue 3).

10. Multiples of 5 that don't end in 5 are multiples of 10 (Clue 1). The factor string is three numbers long (Clue 2), and two of these are 2 and 5. Since two of the numbers in the factor string are the same (Clue 3), the number is $2 \times 2 \times 5 = 20$ or $2 \times 5 \times 5 = 50$. The number is greater than the seventh square number, 49, so 50 is the number.

11. Variable answers. You may want to post some of the best student responses for a Problem of the Week.

12. These numbers are all multiples of 6.

13. These numbers are all multiples of 15.

14. **a.** 2, 4, 8, 16, 32, 64, 128, 256, 512
    b. 1,024

15. This is the only pair of adjacent primes. We know that this is the only such pair because 2 is the only even prime number.

16. There are (infinitely) more odd prime numbers. The only even prime is 2.

Extensions

17. **a.** $4 = 2 + 2, 6 = 3 + 3, 8 = 3 + 5,$
    $10 = 3 + 7$ or $5 + 5, 12 = 5 + 7,$
    $14 = 7 + 7$ or $3 + 11.$

    b. Possible answers: $100 = 3 + 97,$
    $100 = 11 + 89, 100 = 17 + 83,$
    $100 = 29 + 71, 100 = 41 + 59,$
    $100 = 47 + 53$

c. No, because there are no even prime numbers other than 2. If you added the number 2 to an odd prime, the sum would be odd.

18. D   **19.** 210

20. Numbers between twin primes are always divisible by 6. Think about any three consecutive numbers. Of the three, at least one must be divisible by 2, since every second number is divisible by 2. Since the two primes cannot be divisible by 2, the number between them must be. Similarly, in every group of three consecutive numbers, one of them must be divisible by 3, since every third number is divisible by 3. This also has to be the number between the primes, since prime numbers other than 3 itself are not divisible by 3. Because the number between the two primes is divisible by both 2 and 3, it must be divisible by 6.

21. The prime factorization of 36 is $2 \times 2 \times 3 \times 3$. To find all the factors of 36, use every combination of up to two 2's and up to two 3's, and don't forget to include 1! The factors of 36 are 1, 2, 2×2, 3, 3×3, 2×3, $2 \times 2 \times 3$, $2 \times 3 \times 3$, and $2 \times 2 \times 3 \times 3$.

$480 = 2 \times 2 \times 2 \times 2 \times 2 \times 3 \times 5$. The factors are 1, 2, 2×2, $2 \times 2 \times 2$, $2 \times 2 \times 2 \times 2$, $2 \times 2 \times 2 \times 2 \times 2$, 3, 2×3, $2 \times 2 \times 3$, $2 \times 2 \times 2 \times 3$, $2 \times 2 \times 2 \times 2 \times 3$, 5, 2×5, $2 \times 2 \times 5$, $2 \times 2 \times 2 \times 5$, $2 \times 2 \times 2 \times 2 \times 5$, $2 \times 2 \times 2 \times 2 \times 2 \times 5$, 2×5, 3×5, $2 \times 3 \times 5$, $2 \times 2 \times 3 \times 5$, $2 \times 2 \times 2 \times 3 \times 5$, $2 \times 2 \times 2 \times 2 \times 3 \times 5$, and $2 \times 2 \times 2 \times 2 \times 2 \times 3 \times 5$.

22. 1 and 3 must also be factors because 1 and 3 are factors of 6.

23. Then it is also a multiple of 1, 2, 3, 4, and 6 because these are all factors of 12 and will be factors of any multiple of 12.

24. 1, 2, 3, 5, 15, and 30 are also common factors.

25. Boris is correct for 996. The proper factors of 996 are 1, 2, 3, 4, 6, 12, 83, 166, 249, 332, and 498. The sum of the factors is 1,356, which is greater than 996. However, the proper factors of 975 are 1, 3, 5, 13, 15, 25, 39, 65, 75, 195, and 325. The sum of these is 761, which is less than 975, so 975 is not an abundant number, even though it has the same number of factors as 996.

Possible Answers to Mathematical Reflections

1. Numbers have factor pairs, but if the number is a square number, then it has an odd number of factors. One of the factor pairs will have one factor, which is multiplied by itself, so you have only one distinct factor from that pair. For example, 16 is a square number: 4×4 is 16. The factors of 16 are 1, 2, 4, 8, and 16. Thus, 16 has 5 (an odd number) total factors.

2. **a.** The lockers that are touched by only two students have numbers that are prime because these numbers have only two factors.

   b. You know a student touched a certain locker if the student number is a divisor of the locker number.

   c. You know a student touched a certain locker if the locker number is a multiple of the student number.

   d. The lockers open at the end of the problem have square numbers because these numbers have odd numbers of factors.

   e. Since each student touches lockers that are multiples of the student's number, the least common multiple of the two numbers tells you which is the first locker both students touch.

   f. In order to find the last student to touch two different lockers, find the greatest common factor of the two locker numbers.

Answers to Looking Back and Looking Ahead

1. **a.** Yes; during the 30th week of use.

   b. Yes; during the 24th week of use.

2. **a.** There are six factor pairs for 60, but since 1×60 and 60×1 are different arrangements for a spectator looking at the band, there are twelve arrangements. The twelve rectangles have dimensions: 1×60; 2×30; 3×20; 4×15; 5×12; 6×10; 10×6; 12×5; 15×4; 20×3; 30×2; 60×1

   b. Since 61 is prime, the only two arrangements possible are 1×61 and 61×1.

3. a. The LCM is 9,900.

b. The GCF is 3.

c. The factors of Tamika's special number: 1, 2, 3, 4, 6, 11, 12, 22, 33, 44, 66, and 132.

d. A number is even if the prime factor 2 occurs in the prime factorization of the number. If 2 is not in the prime factorization, then the number is odd. So Tamika's number is even, and Cyrah's number is odd.

e. A number is a square number if each prime factor occurs an even number of times in the prime factorization of the number. Cyrah's number is a square number since the prime factors 3 and 5 occur twice each. Tamika's number is not a square number.

4. No, this clue is not enough since 90 has several factors.

a. The least possible secret number is 1. The greatest possible secret number is 90.

b. Brandon is correct. Since the secret number is a factor of 90 and 90 is a factor of 180, then the secret number is a factor of 180.

c. Clue 2 is still not enough to determine the number since 90 has three prime factors— 2, 3, and 5.

d. Yes; since 21 is a multiple of 3 but not a multiple of 2 or 5, the secret number is 3.

5. a. (1) Find all of the factor pairs (stopping when the pairs start to repeat).

(2) Use the prime factorization of the number.

(3) Use clues such as: is the number even, odd, a multiple of 5 or 10, to start a list of the factors.

(4) Make rectangles whose dimensions are the factor pairs of the number.

b. (1) Make a list of the multiples of each number starting with the number itself. The least common multiple is the first multiple to appear in each list. For example, in Question 3, the multiples of Tamika's number are 132; 264; 396; 528; 660; 792; 924; 1,056; 1,188; 1,320; 1,452; 1,584; 1,716; 1,848; 1,980; 2,112; . . . ; 9,768; **9,900**; 10,032; . . . .

The multiples of Cyrah's number are 225; 450; 675; 900; 1,125; 1,350; 1,575; 1,800; 2,025; . . . ; 9,675; **9,900**; 10,125; . . . .

(2) Use the prime factorization. The LCM must contain each of the primes that occur in either number. The prime factor must occur the maximum number of times it occurred in either number. For example, in Question 4, the LCM of Tamika's number and Cyrah's number is $2 \times 2 \times 3 \times 3 \times 5 \times 5 \times 11$, or 9,900.

Discussing both strategies may reveal that the prime factorization may be the most efficient method for finding the LCM. Also refer to Question 2, which is an application that involves finding the LCM of two numbers.

c. (1) List all of the factors of each number and then find the greatest factor that is common to both lists. For example, in Question 3, the factors of Tamika's number are 1, 2, 3, 4, 6, 11, 12, 22, 33, 44, 66, and 132. The factors of Cyrah's number are 1, 3, 5, 9, 15, 25, 45, 75, and 225.

(2) Use the prime factorization. The GCF must contain all of the prime factors that occur in each number. In Question 3, the GCF is 3. It is the only prime that occurs in both factorizations.

6. a. A number is prime if it has no factors other than 1 and itself. One way to do this is to list all the factors of the number.

b. (1) A number is square if its prime factorization contains each prime factor an even number of times. See Question 3 part (e) for an example.

(2) Some students will find all the factors and decide that if the number has an odd number of factors, then it is a square number.

(3) Some students may guess and check to see if the number has a factor pair that contains two equal factors. In this case, they need to check only the numbers 2 through the whole number that is the closest to the square root of the number.

(4) Some students may suggest using the square root button on a calculator.

(5) Some may say it is square if you can make a square whose area (number of unit tiles) is the number.

c. A number is even if 2 is a factor of the number.

d. A number is odd if 2 is not a factor of the number.

7. a. False. This is not true in general. For example, 12 is greater than 10, and 12 has six factors, 1, 2, 3, 4, 6, and 12, while 10 has only four factors: 1, 2, 5, and 10. However, 29 is greater than 6, but 29 has only two factors, 29 and 1, while 6 has four factors: 1, 2, 3, and 6.

b. True. The sum of two odd numbers is always even. An odd number can be split into groups of two with one leftover. Adding two odd numbers will result in two "leftovers," or another group of 2. An illustration is a good way to demonstrate this.

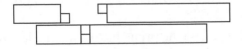

Math Background If X and Y are odd, then $X = 2N + 1$ and $Y = 2M + 1$ where N and M are whole numbers. Thus, $X + Y = 2N + 1 + 2M + 1 = 2N + 2M + 2 = 2(N + M + 1)$. So the sum is even.

c. False. Students may use a geometric argument using rectangular arrangements. For example, $4 \times 3 = 12$. You have four rows of three. Thus the product contains four groups of three, which make an even number of threes in the product.

Math Background If X is even, then $X = 2N$. If Y is odd, then $Y = 2M + 1$. Then $XY = 2N(2M + 1)$. This shows that 2 is factor of XY and thus XY is even.

d. True. For example, if the two numbers are 5 and 17, then the LCM must contain all of the common factors of 5 and 17, but since both are prime, the $LCM = 5 \times 17$.

Math Background The above reasoning is similar to the following general argument: If x and y are prime, x is the only factor of x other than 1, and y is the only factor of y other than 1. Therefore, the first common multiple with both x and y as factors is xy.

e. False. This is not true in general. If $x = 12$ and $y = 18$, then the GCF is 6, and 6 is less than both 12 and 18. On the other hand, if one of the numbers is a factor of the other, that number is the greatest common factor of the two. For example, if $x = 6$ and $y = 12$, then the GCF of 6 and 12 is 6.

My Special Number Project — Final Assessment

For guidelines and examples of students' work, see the Guide to the Unit Project on page 105.

Assigning the Unit Project

The unit project, My Special Number, is an integral part of the assessment in *Prime Time*. The project was introduced at the beginning of the unit. Students were asked to choose a number between 10 and 100 and to write several things about it. After each investigation, students were reminded to use the concepts they learned to write more information about their special numbers.

As the unit ends, each student should decide what form his or her project will take—such as a report, a poem, a story, or a poster. You might suggest that students locate books about numbers in the library. Many books are available that could stimulate ideas. Stress that you expect them to use the vocabulary and concepts from the unit to show everything they know about their special numbers and about what they have learned. Although students should be encouraged to be clever and creative, the emphasis of the project should be on mathematical content.

Tip for the Linguistically Diverse Classroom

Chart Summary The Chart Summary technique is described in detail in *Implementing and Teaching Connected Mathematics*. This technique involves presenting information by condensing it in a pictorial chart with minimal words. For example, the student's special number project could be organized in a chart with headings such as Prime (or Composite), Shape, Proper Factors, Abundant (or Deficient or Perfect), Common Factors, and Common Multiples. Under each of these headings, the student then uses symbols and/or drawings to illustrate how his or her special number relates to each category. For example, if a student's special number is 12, he or she could write the following under the Abundant heading:

Factors of 12: 1, 2, 3, 4, 6
$$1 + 2 + 3 + 4 + 6 = 16$$
and $16 > 12$.

Grading the Unit Project

A possible scoring rubric and two sample projects with teacher comments follow. The first sample is a report; the second is a story.

For ease in grading the Unit Project, two tables are provided, beginning on page 111. One lists proper factors of 2 through 100. The other lists multiples of 10 through 100.

Suggested Scoring Rubric

This rubric for scoring the project employs a scale that runs from 0 to 4, with a 4+ for work that goes beyond what has been asked for in some unique way. You may use this rubric as presented here or modify it to fit your district's requirements for evaluating and reporting students' work and understanding.

4+ EXEMPLARY RESPONSE

- Complete, with clear, coherent explanations
- Shows understanding of the mathematical concepts and procedures
- Satisfies all essential conditions of the problem and goes beyond what is asked for in some unique way

4 COMPLETE RESPONSE

- Complete, with clear, coherent explanations
- Shows understanding of the mathematical concepts and procedures
- Satisfies all essential conditions of the problem

3 REASONABLY COMPLETE RESPONSE

- Reasonably complete; may lack detail in explanations
- Shows understanding of most of the mathematical concepts and procedures
- Satisfies most of the essential conditions of the problem

Sample #1

My Special Number

My special number is 71, I have always liked 71, because it is such an original number.

I'll let you in on the mathematical terms for my special number, 71. For one thing, 71 is a prime number. A prime means that the number has only two factors. It is only divisible by one and itself. Since my number is a prime number, it absolutely is impossible for it to be a composite number. A composite number is a number that has more than two factors.

There are also some mathematical terms that you have probably heard of many times before. For instance, 71, is an odd number. That means that if the last number of a number has the numbers 1,3,5,7, or 9, than the number is odd. Since 71 is odd, than it can't be possibly be even. If

a number is even, it will have either a 0,2,4,6,8 at the end of the number.

Here are a little bit more facts about my number, 71. The factors of 71 are: 1 and 71. Factors are numbers that you can multiply with a number to equal another number. For instance, 71×1=71. 71 is a multiple of 1 and 71. A multiple is a number that increases by the same amount of numbers. It is also the answer to a multiplication problem. The only proper factor for 71 is 1. A proper factor is a number that is a factor of a number, but not the number itself.

Here are some facts about 71 that tell about the sum of its factors. 71 is deficient. That means that the sum of its proper factors add up to less than the number itself. Since 71 is deficient, it can't be abundant of perfect. If a

number is abundant, it means that the sum of the numbers factors add up to more than the number itself. If the number is perfect, it means that the sum of the factors for that number equal up to the number itself.

Here are some facts about the shape of 71. 71 is a rectangle. That means that if you make a block or something, that is 1×71, it will be a rectangle. Since 71 is a rectangle, that means that it is not a square. A square is if you make a block that is, let's say, 6×6, the figure will be a square.

Now I am going to tell you what 71 has in common with other numbers. Well for one thing, 71 does not have any common factors besides the obvious, 1 and 71. Common factors are factors that two or more numbers share. There common multiples of 2 and 71 are: 142,

284, and 426. Common multiples are multiples that two or more numbers share.

Here are some pretty long mathematical terms that most people are not very familiar with. First of all, the last digit of 71, one, has the identity property of 1. The identity property of one means, if you multiply any number by one, it will always equal the number that you started out with. Another long term is the Fundamental Theorem of Arithmetic. The Fundamental Theorem of Arithmatic is a system of multiplication, in which you multiply the factors of a number, in different orders, but always end up with the same product. Relatively Prime numbers are two numbers that can both share the common factor of 1 and only 1. For instance, 71 and 7 are relatively prime numbers,

because the only common factor they share is 1. A near perfect number is a number that is almost perfect. That means that the sum of the factors for the number are one or two numbers off from equaling the multiple. 71 is not a near perfect number. Prime Factorization is when you factor out a number down to only prime numbers. For instance a factor tree is an example of prime factorization. Below is the prime factorization of 71 on a factor tree.

71
← factor tree
1 x 71

A Teacher's Comments on Sample 1

From reading this report, I get a feeling about which ideas this student has made some sense of and some things with which she is still struggling.

The student has used all the listed vocabulary words for this unit and some additional terms *(Identity Property of 1 and near-perfect number)*. If I look at just the words identified as essential to this unit, she seems to have made good sense and usage of *factor, proper factor, common multiples, prime,* and *composite*. The terms not identified as essential *(abundant, deficient, perfect,* and *near-perfect number)* are used effectively. This conclusion can be drawn from the definitions the student has given and the ways she has used the words to explain her number. (Look at the paragraph on prime and composite numbers as an example of what I mean.)

Other words she has used, but less clearly or lacking in detail, are *multiples* (weak explanation), *prime factorization* (right definition, but her prime factorization includes 1, so I have to wonder whether she knows 1 is not prime), and *relatively prime* (right definition, yet she has chosen two prime numbers, so I'm not sure if she knows relatively prime numbers do not have to be prime themselves).

Another weakness of the paper is in her use of the terms *even* and *odd*. Her definition for these words is given as a rule, and she shows no evidence of understanding the mathematics of what it means to be an even or odd number. She also seems confused about the term *common factor*. Her definition is adequate—"factors that two or more numbers share"—but then says 71 does not have any common factors other than 1 and 71. She makes no reference to comparing 71 with another number to look for common factors.

The student shows lack of understanding of the Fundamental Theorem of Arithmetic. Her definition sounds more like a definition for the Commutative Property of Multiplication. There is no mention of the prime factorization of a number.

The part of the paper that leaves me very confused is where she claims "71 is a rectangle" and "since 71 is a rectangle, that means that it is not a square." Part of me wonders whether she is trying to make sense of square numbers, and part of me wonders whether having students build rectangles from a certain number of tiles and on grid paper has caused confusion between the ideas of factors of a number and rectangles.

Considering the paper as a whole, I believe this student shows she has made sense of the ideas in this unit. I am most concerned with her lack of evidence of understanding common multiples because of the importance of this concept. On a 4-point scale, I would give this student a 3.

his binder to a blank sheet of paper. It was exactly 7:00. Bobby picked up his pencil and wrote, my number which is 14 is even cause it is. As Bobby was finishing the last word he heard a knock at the door...

When Bobby opened the door he saw a horrid figure stading before him. The figure spoke. "I am the ghost of math past." Bobby replied "OOOOOK." "You must come with me," the figure said. Bobby followed the figure into the hallway, but as he stepped into the hallway Bobby realized it was no longer the hallway, instead he was standing in his 3rd grade classroom.

Bobby can you tell me why your number is even or odd? "Yes Ms. Shirken, my number which is 14 is even because it is devisable by 2," replied little Bobby, "Very good now can you tell me why it is not odd" asked Ms. Shirken, "Yes Ms. Shirken it is not odd because it is devisable

Sample #2

"And for your homework," said Ms. Hukin, "You need to pick a number and show me the following mathematical things about it."

Bobby hated math homework about as much as he hated Ms. Hukin. Ms. Hukin was 62 and she always wore a sweater and long skirt, even when it was 92 outside and the school's air conditioning is broke - like today. Bobby also hated the way Ms. Hukin always looked at him, she had sharp piercing eyes. It almost felt as if she were trying to stab him with a glance.

Bobby couldn't believe that Ms. Hukin had given them such a huge assignment and only one day to do it in. How was he supposed to get it done? He didn't even understand the stupid thing. Plus his brother was out of town so he had no one to bribe to do it for him. HE WAS GOING TO HAVE TO DO THIS ONE ON HIS OWN!!

Bobby sat down at his desk in his desk in his room and opened

by 2."

Bobby couldn't believe his eyes he just saw himself in the 3rd grade talking to his teacher. "We must go now, further in the past."

Bobby now found himself in his nursery. They were all the way back to when he was a baby. His parent's walked into the room. "Oh what a cute baby," said his mother. "Thats my boy, now for your first math lesson my boy. 14 is a deficient number because all of its factors added up equal less than itself. It is also of course not a perfect number because all of it's factors added up do not equal itself. Got that my boy."

"I always said my father was a little weird," Bobby said to the figure. "You must go back now," said the ghost of math past as he reached over and touched Bobby on the head. All of a sudden Bobby found himself in his own house in his own room. "Cool!" yelled Bobby.
KNOCK KNOCK

"Oh great here we go again!" As Bobby opened the door he saw yet another hideous creature standing before him. It spoke "I am the ghost of of math present, you must come with me." As Bobby stepped into the hallway he found himself standing in Ms. Hukin's room. Bobby looked around and found his desk but he was not sitting there, he must have been in bathroom. Everyone was chanting BOBBY SO STUPID HE DOESN'T EVEN KNOW WHAT A FACTOR IS. "Class settle down," yelled Ms. Hukin. Now Silvia tell me all the factors of 14." "O.K. 1, 2, and 7," said Shirley. "O.K. and tell me the definition of a factor." "OK, factors are the numbers that will go evenly into a certian number." "Very good."

"Oh look here I come," Bobby said as he saw himself walk into the room. "AAAHH there you are Bobby, now sit down and tell me what a multiple is," said Ms. Hukin. "Beats me!" "Oh let me answer!" screamed Shirley. "A multiple

is the sum of a certain number times a certain number, for example 14x2=28 so 28 is a multiple of 14." "Very good, start listening Bobby."

All of a sudden Bobby heard the ghost mumbling to himself "A common multiple is a multiple that 2 different numbers have for example 28 is a common multiple for 2 and 14." "What?" asked Bobby. "Oh sorry I'm studying for a math test," replied the figure.

Bobby blinked for one second and found himself back in his own room. There was a knock at the door.

As Bobby opened the door he saw, yeah you got it another hideous figure. It did not look at Bobby it kept it's head down looking at a paper "14 is a composite number because it has more than one and itself as a factor that is the same reason it's not a prime number, an example of a prime number is 17 it's prime because it's

only factors are 1 and itself. "Math test, huh?" asked Bobby "Yeah oh wait a second here. I am the ghost of math future." "Save it. Listen I want to help you out with your math test. I mean your buddies have been so good to me I figure hay why not." "Great, listen what I don't get is prime factorization." "Oh that's simple; prime factorization is a number broken down into its prime factors for example 14. 14 isn't prime because 7x2=14. 7 and 2 are both prime so thats 14's prime factorization."

All of a sudden the ghost disappeared and Bobby heard his mother calling him. He was back in his desk with the sheet of paper in front of him. He was surprised though because he actually knew what everything ment.

A Teacher's Comments on Sample 2

This piece is very clever with its unique takeoff on *A Christmas Carol*. Yet, what I am most interested in, as a mathematics teacher, is what this student demonstrates about his understanding of the mathematical ideas from this unit.

This student has addressed fewer vocabulary words than the student in the first paper. What is most important is what he says and how he used the words that have been identified as essential. Considering those words first, he seems to have made good sense of *common multiple, factor, prime factorization,* and *prime* and *composite number.* He also has effectively used the words *abundant, deficient, perfect, odd,* and *even numbers.* This conclusion is made from the definition he has given and the ways he used the words in his story. (Look at the paragraph on composite and prime numbers as an example of what I mean.)

The student struggles with the word *multiple*. His example is reasonable, but his definition is confusing. I am not sure what he means when he says, "A multiple is the sum of a certain number times a certain number."

What weakens this paper is the fact that the student did not address two of the essential words from the vocabulary list. There is no evidence of what sense he has made of the ideas of *common factor* and *proper factor*. Because common factor is such an important mathematical idea, I would want to make sure I addressed this with the student.

Considering the paper as a whole, I believe this student shows he has made lots of sense of the ideas in this unit. On a 4-point scale, I would give this student a 3 because of a lack of completeness in not addressing common and proper factors and the weak description of multiples. I believe that if this student were given a chance to revise this paper, with little prompting the paper could easily become a 4.

Unit Project Teacher Aids

Proper Factors

Number	Proper Factors
1	none
2	1
3	1
4	1, 2
5	1
6	1, 2, 3
7	1
8	1, 2, 4
9	1, 3
10	1, 2, 5
11	1
12	1, 2, 3, 4, 6
13	1
14	1, 2, 7
15	1, 3, 5
16	1, 2, 4, 8
17	1
18	1, 2, 3, 6, 9
19	1
20	1, 2, 4, 5, 10
21	1, 3, 7
22	1, 2, 11
23	1
24	1, 2, 3, 4, 6, 8, 12
25	1, 5

Number	Proper Factors
26	1, 2, 13
27	1, 3, 9
28	1, 2, 4, 7, 14
29	1
30	1, 2, 3, 5, 6, 10, 15
31	1
32	1, 2, 4, 8, 16
33	1, 3, 11
34	1, 2, 17
35	1, 5, 7
36	1, 2, 3, 4, 6, 9, 12, 18
37	1
38	1, 2, 19
39	1, 3, 13
40	1, 2, 4, 5, 8, 10, 20
41	1
42	1, 2, 3, 6, 7, 14, 21
43	1
44	1, 2, 4, 11, 22
45	1, 3, 5, 9, 15
46	1, 2, 23
47	1
48	1, 2, 3, 4, 6, 8, 12, 16, 24
49	1, 7
50	1, 2, 5, 10, 25

Proper Factors *(continued)*

Number	Proper Factors	Number	Proper Factors
51	1, 3, 17	76	1, 2, 4, 19, 38
52	1, 2, 4, 13, 26	77	1, 7, 11
53	1	78	1, 2, 3, 6, 13, 26, 39
54	1, 2, 3, 6, 9, 18, 27	79	1
55	1, 5, 11	80	1, 2, 4, 5, 8, 10, 16, 20, 40
56	1, 2, 4, 7, 8, 14, 28	81	1, 3, 9, 27
57	1, 3, 19	82	1, 2, 41
58	1, 2, 29	83	1
59	1	84	1, 2, 3, 4, 6, 7, 12, 14, 21, 28, 42
60	1, 2, 3, 4, 5, 6, 10, 12, 15, 20, 30	85	1, 5, 17
61	1	86	1, 2, 43
62	1, 2, 31	87	1, 3, 29
63	1, 3, 7, 9, 21	88	1, 2, 4, 8, 11, 22, 44
64	1, 2, 4, 8, 16, 32	89	1
65	1, 5, 13	90	1, 2, 3, 5, 6, 9, 10, 15, 18, 30, 45
66	1, 2, 3, 6, 11, 22, 33	91	1, 7, 13
67	1	92	1, 2, 4, 23, 46
68	1, 2, 4, 17, 34	93	1, 3, 31
69	1, 3, 23	94	1, 2, 47
70	1, 2, 5, 7, 10, 14, 35	95	1, 5, 19
71	1	96	1, 2, 3, 4, 6, 8, 12, 16, 24, 32, 48
72	1, 2, 3, 4, 6, 8, 9, 12, 18, 24, 36	97	1
73	1	98	1, 2, 7, 14, 49
74	1, 2, 37	99	1, 3, 9, 11, 33
75	1, 3, 5, 15, 25	100	1, 2, 4, 5, 10, 20, 25, 50

Unit Project Teacher Aids

Multiples

Numbers	10	11	12	13	14	15	16	17	18	19	20	21	22	23	24
×2	20	22	24	26	28	30	32	34	36	38	40	42	44	46	48
×3	30	33	36	39	42	45	48	51	54	57	60	63	66	69	72
×4	40	44	48	52	56	60	64	68	72	76	80	84	88	92	96
×5	50	55	60	65	70	75	80	85	90	95	100	105	110	115	120
×6	60	66	72	78	84	90	96	102	108	114	120	126	132	138	144
×7	70	77	84	91	98	105	112	119	126	133	140	147	154	161	168
×8	80	88	96	104	112	120	128	136	144	152	160	168	176	184	192
×9	90	99	108	117	126	135	144	153	162	171	180	189	198	207	216
×10	100	110	120	130	140	150	160	170	180	190	200	210	220	230	240

Numbers	25	26	27	28	29	30	31	32	33	34	35	36	37	38	39
×2	50	52	54	56	58	60	62	64	66	68	70	72	74	76	78
×3	75	78	81	84	87	90	93	96	99	102	105	108	111	114	117
×4	100	104	108	112	116	120	124	128	132	136	140	144	148	152	156
×5	125	130	135	140	145	150	155	160	165	170	175	180	185	190	195
×6	150	156	162	168	174	180	186	192	198	204	210	216	222	228	234
×7	175	182	189	196	203	210	217	224	231	238	245	252	259	266	273
×8	200	208	216	224	232	240	248	256	264	272	280	288	296	304	312
×9	225	234	243	252	261	270	279	288	297	306	315	324	333	342	351
×10	250	260	270	280	290	300	310	320	330	340	350	360	370	380	390

Numbers	40	41	42	43	44	45	46	47	48	49	50	51	52	53	54
×2	80	82	84	86	88	90	92	94	96	98	100	102	104	106	108
×3	120	123	126	129	132	135	138	141	144	147	150	153	156	159	162
×4	160	164	168	172	176	180	184	188	192	196	200	204	208	212	216
×5	200	205	210	215	220	225	230	235	240	245	250	255	260	265	270
×6	240	246	252	258	264	270	276	282	288	294	300	306	312	318	324
×7	280	287	294	301	308	315	322	329	336	343	350	357	364	371	378
×8	320	328	336	344	352	360	368	376	384	392	400	408	416	424	432
×9	360	369	378	387	396	405	414	423	432	441	450	459	468	477	486
×10	400	410	420	430	440	450	460	470	480	490	500	510	520	530	540

Numbers	55	56	57	58	59	60	61	62	63	64	65	66	67	68	69
×2	110	112	114	116	118	120	122	124	126	128	130	132	134	136	138
×3	165	168	171	174	177	180	183	186	189	192	195	198	201	204	207
×4	220	224	228	232	236	240	244	248	252	256	260	264	268	272	276
×5	275	280	285	290	295	300	305	310	315	320	325	330	335	340	345
×6	330	336	342	348	354	360	366	372	378	384	390	396	402	408	414
×7	385	392	399	406	413	420	427	434	441	448	455	462	469	476	483
×8	440	448	456	464	472	480	488	496	504	512	520	528	536	544	552
×9	495	504	513	522	531	540	549	558	567	576	585	594	603	612	621
×10	550	560	570	580	590	600	610	620	630	640	650	660	670	680	690

Multiples *(continued)*

Numbers	70	71	72	73	74	75	76	77	78	79	80	81	82	83	84
×2	140	142	144	146	148	150	152	154	156	158	160	162	164	166	168
×3	210	213	216	219	222	225	228	231	234	237	240	243	246	249	252
×4	280	284	288	292	296	300	304	308	312	316	320	324	328	332	336
×5	350	355	360	365	370	375	380	385	390	395	400	405	410	415	420
×6	420	426	432	438	444	450	456	462	468	474	480	486	492	498	504
×7	490	497	504	511	518	525	532	539	546	553	560	567	574	581	588
×8	560	568	576	584	592	600	608	616	624	632	640	648	656	664	672
×9	630	639	648	657	666	675	684	693	702	711	720	729	738	747	756
×10	700	710	720	730	740	750	760	770	780	790	800	810	820	830	840

Numbers	85	86	87	88	89	90	91	92	93	94	95	96	97	98	99
×2	170	172	174	176	178	180	182	184	186	188	190	192	194	196	198
×3	255	258	261	264	267	270	273	276	279	282	285	288	291	294	297
×4	340	344	348	352	356	360	364	368	372	376	380	384	388	392	396
×5	425	430	435	440	445	450	455	460	465	470	475	480	485	490	495
×6	510	516	522	528	534	540	546	552	558	564	570	576	582	588	594
×7	595	602	609	616	623	630	637	644	651	658	665	672	679	686	693
×8	680	688	696	704	712	720	728	736	744	752	760	768	776	784	792
×9	765	774	783	792	801	810	819	828	837	846	855	864	873	882	891
×10	850	860	870	880	890	900	910	920	930	940	950	960	970	980	990

Numbers	100
×2	200
×3	300
×4	400
×5	500
×6	600
×7	700
×8	800
×9	900
×10	1000

The student edition pages for this
investigation begin on the next page.

Notes

Unit Project

My Special Number

At the beginning of this unit, you chose a special number and wrote several things about it in your journal. As you worked through the investigations, you used the concepts you learned to write new things about your number.

Now it is time for you to show off your special number. Write a story, compose a poem, make a poster, or find some other way to highlight your number.

Your teacher will use your project to determine how well you understand the concepts in this unit, so be sure to include all the things you have learned while working through the investigations. You may want to start by looking back through your journal to find the things you wrote after each investigation. In your project, be sure you use all the vocabulary your teacher has asked you to record in your journals for *Prime Time*.

STUDENT PAGE

Notes _____

_____

_____

_____

Looking Back and Looking Ahead

Unit Review

While working on the problems in this unit, you investigated some important properties of whole numbers. Finding factors and multiples of numbers and identifying prime numbers helps in answering questions about clocks and calendars, puzzles and games, and rectangular patterns of tiles. Factoring also focuses attention on the properties of even and odd numbers, square numbers, greatest common factors, and least common multiples.

Go Online
PHSchool.com

For: Vocabulary Review Puzzle
Web Code: amj-1051

Use Your Understanding: Number Patterns

Test your understanding of multiples, factors, and prime numbers, by solving the following problems.

1. The Red Top Taxi company wants to keep its cars in good operating condition. It has a schedule for regular maintenance checks on each car. Oil is to be changed once every 6 weeks. Brakes are to be inspected and repaired every 10 weeks.

   a. After a new cab is put in service, is there ever a week when that cab is scheduled for both an oil change and a brake inspection? If so, what is the first such time?

   b. Suppose the oil change time is extended to 8 weeks and the brake inspection to 12 weeks. Is there ever a week when the cab is due for both an oil change and brake inspection? If so, when will such a coincidence first occur?

Looking Back and Looking Ahead   **71**

Notes _____

_____

_____

_____

2. The Mystate University marching band consists of 60 members. The band director wants to arrange the band into a rectangular array for the halftime activities.

   a. In how many ways can she arrange the band? Make a sketch of each arrangement.

   b. How many rectangular arrangements are possible if the band adds one member and becomes a 61-member band?

3. The prime factorization of Tamika's special number is $2 \times 2 \times 3 \times 11$ and the prime factorization of Cyrah's special number is $3 \times 3 \times 5 \times 5$.

   a. What is the least common multiple of the two special numbers?

   b. What is the greatest common factor of the two special numbers?

   c. List all the factors of Tamika's number.

   d. Is Tamika's number even or odd? Is Cyrah's number even or odd?

   e. Is Tamika's number a square number? Is Cyrah's number a square number?

4. Shani gave three clues for her secret number.

   Clue 1 *My number is a factor of 90.*

   Can you determine what Shani's secret number is?

   a. What is the smallest Shani's number can be? What is the largest Shani's number can be?

   b. Brandon says the secret number must also be a factor of 180. Is he correct?

   Clue 2 *My number is prime.*

   c. Now can you determine what the secret number is?

   Clue 3 *Twenty-one is a multiple of my secret number.*

   d. Now can you determine what the secret number is?

Notes _____

_____

_____

_____

Explain Your Reasoning

To answer Questions 1–4 you had to use knowledge of factors and multiples of a number.

5. What strategies can be used to find
   a. all the factors of a number?
   b. the least common multiple of two numbers?
   c. the greatest common factor of two numbers?

6. How you can you decide whether a number is a(n)
   a. prime number?
   b. square number?
   c. even number?
   d. odd number?

7. Decide whether each statement is *true* or *false*. Explain your reasoning. (A statement is true if it is correct for *every* pair of numbers. If you can find a pair of numbers that makes the statement incorrect, then the statement is false.)
   a. If a number is greater than a second number, then the first number has more factors than the second number.
   b. The sum of two odd numbers is even.
   c. The product of an even number and an odd number is odd.
   d. The least common multiple of two different prime numbers is the product of those numbers.
   e. The greatest common factor of two numbers is less than either of those numbers.

Look Ahead

You will use ideas about factors, multiples, and primes in many future units of *Connected Mathematics*, especially those that deal with properties of other numbers like fractions and decimals.

Notes _____

_____

_____

_____

English / Spanish Glossary

A

abundant number A number for which the sum of all its proper factors is greater than the number itself. For example, 24 is an abundant number because its proper factors, 1, 2, 3, 4, 6, 8, and 12, add to 36.

número abundante Un número con factores propios que sumados resultan en un número mayor que el número mismo. Por ejemplo, 24 es un número abundante porque la suma de sus factores propios, 1, 2, 3, 4, 6, 8 y 12, es 36.

C

common factor A factor that two or more numbers share. For example, 7 is a common factor of 14 and 35 because 7 is a factor of 14 ($14 = 7 \times 2$) and 7 is a factor of 35 ($35 = 7 \times 5$).

factor común Un factor que es compartido por dos o más números. Por ejemplo, 7 es factor común de 14 y 35 porque 7 es factor de 14 ($14 = 7 \times 2$) y 7 es factor de 35 ($35 = 7 \times 5$).

common multiple A multiple that two or more numbers share. For example, the first few multiples of 5 are 5, 10, 15, 20, 25, 30, 35, 40, 45, 50, 55, 60, 65, and 70. The first few multiples of 7 are 7, 14, 21, 28, 35, 42, 49, 56, 63, 70, 77, 84, 91, and 98. From these lists, we can see that two common multiples of 5 and 7 are 35 and 70.

múltiplo común Un múltiplo compartido por dos o más números. Por ejemplo, los primeros múltiplos de 5 son 5, 10, 15, 20, 25, 30, 35, 40, 45, 50, 55, 60, 65 y 70. Los primeros múltiplos de 7 son 7, 14, 21, 28, 35, 42, 49, 56, 63, 70, 77, 84, 91 y 98. Estas listas nos indican que dos múltiplos comunes de 5 y 7 son el 35 y el 70.

composite number A whole number with factors other than itself and 1 (that is, a whole number that is not prime). Some composite numbers are 6, 12, 20, and 1,001.

número compuesto Un número entero con otros factores además del número mismo y el 1 (es decir, un número entero que no es primo). Algunos números compuestos son 6, 12, 20 y 1,001.

conjecture A guess about a pattern or relationship based on observations.

conjetura Suposición acerca de un patrón o relación, basada en observaciones.

Notes

deficient number A number for which the sum of all its proper factors is less than the number itself. For example, 14 is a deficient number because its proper factors, 1, 2, and 7, add to 10. All prime numbers are deficient.

número deficiente Un número con factores propios que sumados resultan en un número menor que el número mismo. Por ejemplo, 14 es un número deficiente porque la suma de sus factores 1, 2 y 7 equivale a 10. Todos los números primos son deficientes.

dimensions The dimensions of a rectangle are the lengths of its sides. For example, the rectangle below has side lengths of 5 and 3. We can refer to this rectangle as a 5 × 3 rectangle.

dimensiones Las dimensiones de un rectángulo son las longitudes de sus lados. Por ejemplo, el rectángulo de abajo tiene longitudes de lados de 3 y 5. Podemos referirnos a este rectángulo como un rectángulo de 5 × 3.

divisor A number that divides a given number leaving a zero remainder. For example, 5 is a divisor of 20 since 20 ÷ 5 = 4 has a remainder of 0. A divisor of a given number is also known as a factor of that number. Another way to determine if 5 is a divisor of 20 is to ask whether there is a whole number that, when multiplied by 5, gives 20. The number is 4. 5 × 4 = 20.

divisor Número que divide a otro número sin dejar ningún resto. Por ejemplo, 5 es un divisor de 20 porque 20 ÷ 5 = 4 tiene resto cero. El divisor de un número determinado también se conoce como un factor de ese número. Otra manera de determinar si 5 es divisor de 20 es preguntando si hay un número entero que, al ser multiplicado por 5, dé 20. El número es 4. 5 × 4 = 20.

E

even number A multiple of 2. When you divide an even number by 2, the remainder is 0. Examples of even numbers are 0, 2, 4, 6, 8, and 10.

número par Un múltiplo de 2. Cuando divides un número par por 2, el resto es 0. Los siguientes son ejemplos de números pares: 0, 2, 4, 6, 8 y 10.

exponent The small raised number that tells how many times a factor is used. For example, 5^3 means 5 × 5 × 5. 3 is the exponent.

exponente El pequeño número elevado que dice cuántas veces se usa un factor. Por ejemplo, 5^3 significa 5 × 5 × 5. 3 es el exponente.

English/Spanish Glossary **75**

Notes

F

factor One of two or more whole numbers that are multiplied to get a product. For example, 13 and 4 are both factors of 52 because $13 \times 4 = 52$.

factor Uno de dos o más números enteros que se multiplican para obtener un producto. Por ejemplo, tanto 13 como 4 son factores de 52 porque $13 \times 4 = 52$.

factor pair Two whole numbers that are multiplied to get a product. For example, in the pair 13, 4 is a factor pair of 52 because $13 \times 4 = 52$.

par de factores Dos números enteros que se multiplican para obtener un producto. Por ejemplo, el par 13, 4 es un par factor de 52 porque $13 \times 4 = 52$.

factorization A product of numbers, perhaps with some repetitions, resulting in the desired number. A number can have many factorizations. For example, two factorizations of 60 are 3×20 and $2 \times 2 \times 15$.

factorización Producto de números, con posibles repeticiones, que resultan en el número deseado. Un número puede tener muchas factorizaciones. Por ejemplo, dos factorizaciones de 60 son 3×20 y $2 \times 2 \times 15$.

Fundamental Theorem of Arithmetic The theorem stating that, except for the order of the factors, every whole number greater than 1 can be factored into prime factors in only one way.

Teorema fundamental de la aritmética Teorema que enuncia que, salvo por el orden de los factores, todos los números enteros mayores de 1 pueden descomponerse en factores primos de una sola manera.

G

greatest common factor The greatest factor that two or more numbers share. For example, 1, 2, 3, and 6 are common factors of 12 and 30, but 6 is the greatest common factor.

máximo común factor El factor mayor que comparten dos o más números. Por ejemplo, 1, 2, 3 y 6 son factores comunes de 12 y 30, pero 6 es el máximo común factor.

L

least common multiple The least multiple that two or more numbers share. Common multiples of 6 and 8 include 24, 48, and 72, but 24 is the least common multiple.

mínimo común múltiplo El múltiplo menor que comparten dos o más números. Los múltiplos comunes de 6 y 8 incluyen 24, 48 y 72, pero 24 es el mínimo común múltiplo.

Notes _____

_____

_____

_____

multiple The product of a given whole number and another whole number. For example, some multiples of 3 are 3, 6, 9, and 12. Note that if a number is a multiple of 3, then 3 is a factor of the number. For example, 12 is a multiple of 3, and 3 is a factor of 12.

múltiplo El producto de un número entero dado y otro número entero. Por ejemplo, algunos múltiplos de 3 son 3, 6, 9 y 12. Observa que si un número es múltiplo de 3, entonces 3 es factor de ese número. Por ejemplo, 12 es múltiplo de 3, y 3 es factor de 12.

near-perfect number A number for which the sum of all its proper factors is one less than the number. All powers of 2 are near-perfect numbers. For example, 32 is a near-perfect number because its proper factors, 1, 2, 4, 8, and 16, add to 31.

número casi perfecto Un número con factores propios que sumados resultan en 1 menos que ese número. Todas las potencias de 2 son números casi perfectos. Por ejemplo, 32 es un número casi perfecto porque sus factores propios 1, 2, 4, 8 y 16 suman 31.

odd number A whole number that is not a multiple of 2. When an odd number is divided by 2, the remainder is 1. Examples of odd numbers are 1, 3, 5, 7, and 9.

número impar Un número entero que no es múltiplo de 2. Cuando un número impar se divide por 2, el resto es 1. Los siguientes son ejemplos de números impares: 1, 3, 5, 7 y 9.

perfect number A number for which the sum of all its proper factors is the number itself. For example, 6 is a perfect number because its proper factors, 1, 2, and 3, add to 6.

número perfecto Un número con factores propios que, cuando se suman, el resultado es ese número exacto. Por ejemplo, 6 es un número perfecto porque la suma de sus factores propios, 1, 2 y 3, es 6.

prime factorization A product of prime numbers, perhaps with some repetitions, resulting in the desired number. For example, the prime factorization of 7,007 is $7 \times 7 \times 11 \times 13$. The prime factorization of a number is unique except for the order of the factors.

descomposición en factores primos Un producto de números primos, con posibles repeticiones, que resulta en el número deseado. Por ejemplo, la descomposición en factores primos de 7,007 es $7 \times 7 \times 11 \times 13$. La descomposición en factores primos de un número es única salvo por el orden de los factores.

STUDENT PAGE

Notes _____

_____

_____

_____

prime number A number with exactly two factors, 1 and the number itself. Examples of primes are 11, 17, 53, and 101. The number 1 is not a prime number because it has only one factor.

número primo Un número que tiene exactamente dos factores: 1 y él mismo. Los siguientes son ejemplos de números primos: 11, 17, 53 y 101. El número 1 no es un número primo porque tiene sólo un factor.

proper factors All the factors of a number, except the number itself. For example, the proper factors of 16 are 1, 2, 4, and 8.

factores propios Todos los factores de un número salvo el número mismo. Por ejemplo, los factores propios de 16 son 1, 2, 4 y 8.

relatively prime numbers A pair of numbers with no common factors except for 1. For example, 20 and 33 are relatively prime because the factors of 20 are 1, 2, 4, 5, 10, and 20, while the factors of 33 are 1, 3, 11, and 33. Notice that neither 20 nor 33 is itself a prime number.

números relativamente primos Par de números que no tienen factores comunes salvo 1. Por ejemplo, 20 y 33 son números relativamente primos porque los factores de 20 son 1, 2, 4, 5, 10 y 20 mientras que los factores de 33 son 1, 3, 11 y 33. Observa que ni el 20 ni el 33 son en sí mismos números primos.

square number A number that is a result of the product of a number multiplied by itself. For example, 9 and 64 are square numbers because $9 = 3 \times 3$ and $64 = 8 \times 8$. A square number represents a number of square tiles that can be arranged to form a square.

número al cuadrado Número que es el resultado del producto de un número multiplicado por sí mismo. Por ejemplo, 9 y 64 son números al cuadrado porque $9 = 3 \times 3$ y $64 = 8 \times 8$. Un número al cuadrado representa un número de mosaicos cuadrados que se pueden colocar para formar un cuadrado.

Notes

Venn diagram A diagram in which overlapping circles are used to show relationships among sets of objects that have certain attributes. Two examples are shown below.

diagrama de Venn Un diagrama en el que se usan círculos superpuestos para representar relaciones entre conjuntos de objetos que tienen ciertos atributos. A continuación se muestran dos ejemplos. En uno se muestran factores de 24 y factores de 60, y en el otro se muestran múltiplos de 24 y múltiplos de 60.

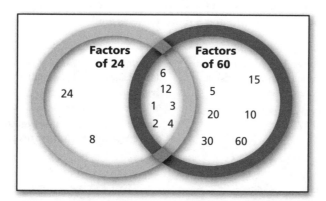

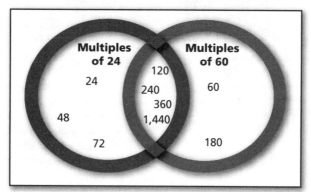

English/Spanish Glossary   **79**

Notes _____

_____

_____

_____

Academic Vocabulary

The following terms are important to your understanding of the mathematics in this unit. Knowing and using these words will help you in thinking, reasoning, representing, communicating your ideas, and making connections across ideas. When these words make sense to you, the investigations and problems will make more sense as well.

D

determine To use the given information and any related facts to find a value or make a decision.
related terms: decide, find, calculate, conclude

Sample: What is one way to determine the prime factorization of 27?

I could use a factor tree to determine the prime factorization of 27.

I can also divide 27 by prime numbers until I have a prime quotient. For example, 3 is prime and $27 \div 3 = 9$. Since 9 is not prime, I continue to divide. $9 \div 3 = 3$ and 3 is prime. The prime factors for 27 are $3 \times 3 \times 3$.

determinar Usar la información dada y cualesquiera datos relacionados para hallar un valor o tomar una decisión.
términos relacionados: decidir, hallar, calcular, concluir

Ejemplo: ¿Cuál es una forma de determinar la descomposición en factores primos de 27?

Podría usar un árbol de factores para determinar la descomposición en factores primos de 27.

También puedo dividir 27 por números primos hasta obtener el cociente primo. Por ejemplo, 3 es un número primo y $27 \div 3 = 9$. Puesto que 9 no es un número primo, puedo continuar con la división. $9 \div 3 = 3$ y 3 es un número primo. Los factores primos de 27 son $3 \times 3 \times 3$.

E

explain To give facts and details that make an idea easier to understand. Explaining can involve a written summary supported by a diagram, chart, table, or a combination of these.
related terms: analyze, clarify, describe, justify, tell

Sample: Amara is thinking of a number that is the least common multiple of 5 and 6. What is the number? Explain your reasoning.

Multiples of 5: 5, 10, 15, 20, 25, 30, 35...
Multiples of 6: 6, 12, 18, 24, 30, 36, 42...
The first common multiple is 30. So, Amara's number is 30.

explicar Dar hechos y detalles que hacen que una idea sea más fácil de comprender. Explicar puede implicar un resumen escrito apoyado por hechos, un diagrama, una gráfica, una tabla o una combinación de éstos.
términos relacionados: analizar, aclarar, describir, justificar, decir

Ejemplo: Amara está pensando en un número que es el mínimo común múltiplo de 5 y 6. ¿Cuál es el número? Explica tu razonamiento.

Múltiplos de 5: 5, 10, 15, 20, 25, 30, 35...
Múltiplos de 6: 6, 12, 18, 24, 30, 36, 42...
El primer común múltiplo es 30. Así que el número de Amara es 30.

80 Prime Time

Notes

justify To support your answers with reasons or examples

related terms: validate, explain, defend

Sample: Jeffrey claims that 12 and 14 are relatively prime numbers. Is Jeffrey correct? Justify your answer.

Jeffrey is not correct. The Venn diagram shows that 12 and 14 have both 1 and 2 as common factors. Since 12 and 14 share two factors they cannot be relatively prime.

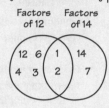

justificar Apoyar tus respuestas con razones o ejemplos.

términos relacionados: validar, explicar, defender

Ejemplo: Jeffrey afirma que 12 y 14 son números primos entre sí. ¿Es correcta la afirmación de Jeffrey? Justifica tu respuesta.

La afirmación de Jeffrey no es correcta. El diagrama de Venn muestra que 12 y 14 tienen 1 y 2 como factores comunes. Puesto que 12 y 14 comparten dos factores no pueden ser números primos entre sí.

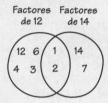

represent To stand for or take the place of something else. Symbols, equations, charts, and tables are often used to represent particular situations.

related terms: symbolize, stand for

Sample: Which of the following sets of numbers represents the factors of 16? Explain.

A. {1, 2, 3, 4, 9, 16}   C. {1, 2, 4, 8, 16}

B. {2, 4, 8}   D. {16, 32, 48, 64}

Set C represents the factors of 16. Set A does not represent the factors of 16 since 3 and 9 are not factors of 16. Set B does not include 1 and 16, which are factors of 16. Set D contains multiples of 16 instead of factors of 16.

representar Significar o tomar el lugar de algo más. Con frecuencia se usan símbolos, ecuaciones, gráficas y tablas para representar situaciones particulares.

términos relacionados: simbolizar, significar

Ejemplo: ¿Cuál de los siguientes conjuntos de números representa los factores de 16? Explica tu respuesta.

A. {1, 2, 3, 4, 9, 16}   C. {1, 2, 4, 8, 16}

B. {2, 4, 8}   D. {16, 32, 48, 64}

El conjunto C representa los factores de 16. El conjunto A no representa los factores de 16 puesto que 3 y 9 no son factores de 16. El conjunto B no incluye 1 y 16, los cuales son factores de 16. El conjunto D contiene múltiplos de 16 en lugar de factores de 16.

Academic Vocabulary **81**

Notes

Index

Notes

STUDENT PAGE

Index

Notes

Acknowledgments

Team Credits

The people who made up the **Connected Mathematics2** team—representing editorial, editorial services, design services, and production services—are listed below. Bold type denotes core team members.

Leora Adler, Judith Buice, Kerry Cashman, Patrick Culleton, Sheila DeFazio, Richard Heater, **Barbara Hollingdale, Jayne Holman,** Karen Holtzman, **Etta Jacobs,** Christine Lee, Carolyn Lock, Catherine Maglio, **Dotti Marshall,** Rich McMahon, Eve Melnechuk, Kristin Mingrone, Terri Mitchell, **Marsha Novak,** Irene Rubin, Donna Russo, Robin Samper, Siri Schwartzman, **Nancy Smith,** Emily Soltanoff, **Mark Tricca,** Paula Vergith, Roberta Warshaw, Helen Young

Additional Credits

Diana Bonfilio, Mairead Reddin, Michael Torocsik, nSight, Inc.

Technical Illustration

WestWords, Inc.

Cover Design

tom white.images

Photos

2, Frank Cezus/Getty Images, Inc.; 3 t, Adrian Peacock/ImageState; 3 b, Peter Hvizdak/ The Image Works; 5, Richard Haynes; 6 t, Michael Newman/PhotoEdit; 6 bl, BananaStock/SuperStock; 6 bm, Michael Newman/PhotoEdit; 6 br, Ryan McVay/Getty Images, Inc.; 10, Declan McCullagh Photography; 13, Richard Haynes; 17, Frank Cezus/Getty Images, Inc.; 22, Rex Butcher/Getty Images, Inc.; 25, Richard Haynes; 32, Bettmann/Corbis; 37, Lester Lefkowitz/Corbis; 38, Ron Chapple/Thinkstock/Alamy Images; 41, Ariel Skelley/Corbis; 42, joSon/SuperStock; 47, ©1991 by Sydney Harris, From "You Want Proof, I'll Give You Proof!", WH. Freeman, New York; 57, Peter Usbeck/Alamy Images; 58, David Young-Wolff/PhotoEdit; 65, Digital Vision/Getty Images, Inc.; 66, Richard Haynes

Data Sources

Information on Prime Numbers on pages 10-11 from THE NEW YORK TIMES, August 8, 2002. Copyright © 2002 The New York Times Company.

Note: Every effort has been made to locate the copyright owner of the material reprinted in this book. Omissions brought to our attention will be corrected in subsequent editions.

Notes _____

_____

_____

_____

Labsheet 1.1

Factor Game Boards

1	2	3	4	5
6	7	8	9	10
11	12	13	14	15
16	17	18	19	20
21	22	23	24	25
26	27	28	29	30

1	2	3	4	5
6	7	8	9	10
11	12	13	14	15
16	17	18	19	20
21	22	23	24	25
26	27	28	29	30

1	2	3	4	5
6	7	8	9	10
11	12	13	14	15
16	17	18	19	20
21	22	23	24	25
26	27	28	29	30

1	2	3	4	5
6	7	8	9	10
11	12	13	14	15
16	17	18	19	20
21	22	23	24	25
26	27	28	29	30

Labsheet 1.2

Table for Recording First Moves

Possible First Move	Proper Factors	My Score	Opponent Score
1			
2			
3			
4			
5			
6			
7			
8			
9			
10			
11			
12			
13			
14			
15			
16			
17			
18			
19			
20			
21			
22			
23			
24			
25			
26			
27			
28			
29			
30			

Labsheet 1.3

Product Game Boards

1	2	3	4	5	6
7	8	9	10	12	14
15	16	18	20	21	24
25	27	28	30	32	35
36	40	42	45	48	49
54	56	63	64	72	81

1	2	3	4	5	6
7	8	9	10	12	14
15	16	18	20	21	24
25	27	28	30	32	35
36	40	42	45	48	49
54	56	63	64	72	81

Factors:

1   2   3   4   5   6   7   8   9

Factors:

1   2   3   4   5   6   7   8   9

1	2	3	4	5	6
7	8	9	10	12	14
15	16	18	20	21	24
25	27	28	30	32	35
36	40	42	45	48	49
54	56	63	64	72	81

1	2	3	4	5	6
7	8	9	10	12	14
15	16	18	20	21	24
25	27	28	30	32	35
36	40	42	45	48	49
54	56	63	64	72	81

Factors:

1   2   3   4   5   6   7   8   9

Factors:

1   2   3   4   5   6   7   8   9

Labsheet 2.3A

A and B Venn Diagrams

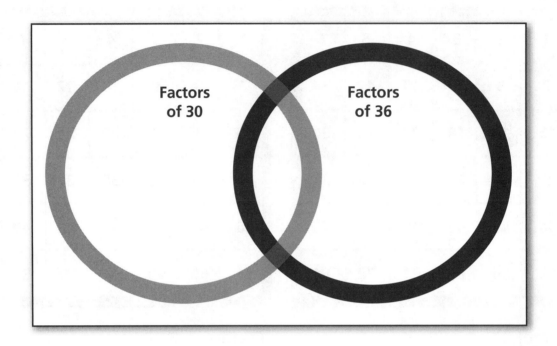

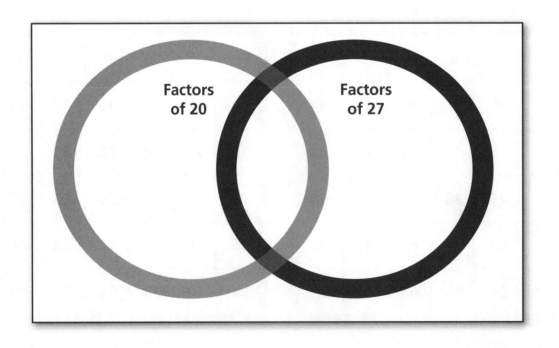

Labsheet 2.3B

C and D Venn Diagrams

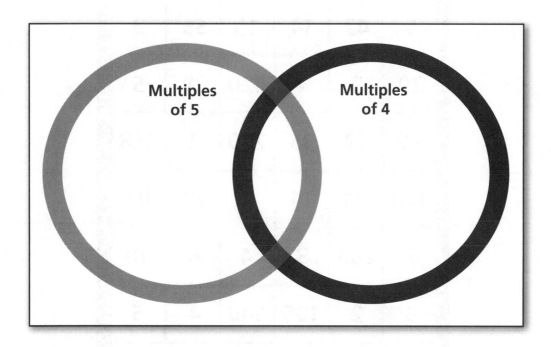

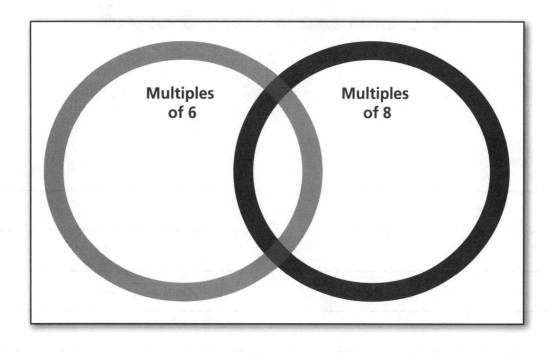

Labsheet 4.1

The Product Puzzle

5	42	14	15	56	3
20	3	4	420	28	5
70	12	35	210	2	168
120	24	14	2	28	84
7	280	3	4	6	10
3	2	105	140	4	5
20	40	8	21	2	7

_____   _____

_____   _____

_____   _____

_____   _____

_____   _____

Labsheet 5.1A

Open Locker

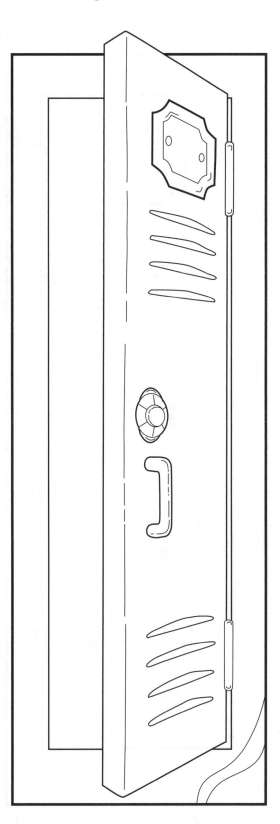

Labsheet 5.1B

Closed Locker

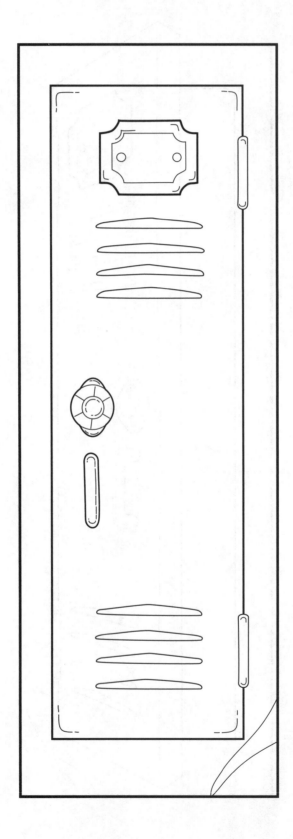

PACING: _____

Mathematical Goals

_____

_____

_____

_____

Launch

_____

_____

_____

_____

_____

_____

_____

Materials

Explore

_____

_____

_____

_____

_____

_____

_____

Materials

Summarize

_____

_____

_____

_____

_____

_____

_____

Materials

Glossary

abundant number A number for which the sum of all its proper factors is greater than the number itself. For example, 24 is an abundant number because its proper factors, 1, 2, 3, 4, 6, 8, and 12, add to 36.

common factor A factor that two or more numbers share. For example, 7 is a common factor of 14 and 35 because 7 is a factor of 14 (14 = 7 × 2) and 7 is a factor of 35 (35 = 7 × 5).

common multiple A multiple that two or more numbers share. For example, the first few multiples of 5 are 5, 10, 15, 20, 25, 30, 35, 40, 45, 50, 55, 60, 65, and 70. The first few multiples of 7 are 7, 14, 21, 28, 35, 42, 49, 56, 63, 70, 77, 84, 91, and 98. From these lists, we can see that two common multiples of 5 and 7 are 35 and 70.

composite number A whole number with factors other than itself and 1 (that is, a whole number that is not prime). Some composite numbers are 6, 12, 20, and 1,001.

conjecture A guess about a pattern or relationship based on observations.

D

deficient number A number for which the sum of all its proper factors is less than the number itself. For example, 14 is a deficient number because its proper factors, 1, 2, and 7, add to 10. All prime numbers are deficient.

dimensions The dimensions of a rectangle are the lengths of its sides. For example, the rectangle below has side lengths of 5 and 3. We can refer to this rectangle as a 5 × 3 rectangle.

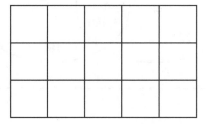

divisor A number that divides a given number leaving a zero remainder. For example, 5 is a divisor of 20 since 20 ÷ 5 = 4 has a remainder of 0. A divisor of a given number is also known as a factor of that number. Another way to determine if 5 is a divisor of 20 is to ask whether there is a whole number that, when multiplied by 5, gives 20. The number is 4. 5 × 4 = 20.

even number A multiple of 2. When you divide an even number by 2, the remainder is 0. Examples of even numbers are 0, 2, 4, 6, 8, and 10.

exponent The small raised number that tells how many times a factor is used. For example, 5^3 means 5 × 5 × 5. 3 is the exponent.

factor One of two or more whole numbers that are multiplied to get a product. For example, 13 and 4 are both factors of 52 because 13 × 4 = 52.

factor pair Two whole numbers that are multiplied to get a product. For example, the pair 13, 4 is a factor pair of 52 because 13 × 4 = 52.

factorization A product of numbers, perhaps with some repetitions, resulting in the desired number. A number can have many factorizations. For example, two factorizations of 60 are 3 × 20 and 2 × 2 × 15.

Fundamental Theorem of Arithmetic The theorem stating that, except for the order of the factors, every whole number greater than 1 can be factored into prime factors in only one way.

greatest common factor The greatest factor that two or more numbers share. For example, 1, 2, 3, and 6 are common factors of 12 and 30, but 6 is the greatest common factor.

least common multiple The least multiple that two or more numbers share. Common multiples of 6 and 8 include 24, 48, and 72, but 24 is the least common multiple.

multiple The product of a given whole number and another whole number. For example, some multiples of 3 are 3, 6, 9, and 12. Note that if a number is a multiple of 3, then 3 is a factor of the number. For example, 12 is a multiple of 3, and 3 is a factor of 12.

near-perfect number A number for which the sum of all its proper factors is one less than the number. All powers of 2 are near-perfect numbers. For example, 32 is a near-perfect number because its proper factors, 1, 2, 4, 8, and 16, add to 31.

odd number A whole number that is not a multiple of 2. When an odd number is divided by 2, the remainder is 1. Examples of odd numbers are 1, 3, 5, 7, and 9.

perfect number A number for which the sum of all its proper factors is the number itself. For example, 6 is a perfect number because its proper factors, 1, 2, and 3, add to 6.

prime factorization A product of prime numbers, perhaps with some repetitions, resulting in the desired number. For example, the prime factorization of 7,007 is 7 × 7 × 11 × 13. The prime factorization of a number is unique except for the order of the factors.

prime number A number with exactly two factors, 1 and the number itself. Examples of primes are 11, 17, 53, and 101. The number 1 is not a prime number because it has only one factor.

proper factors All the factors of a number, except the number itself. For example, the proper factors of 16 are 1, 2, 4, and 8.

relatively prime numbers A pair of numbers with no common factors except for 1. For example, 20 and 33 are relatively prime because the factors of 20 are 1, 2, 4, 5, 10, and 20, while the factors of 33 are 1, 3, 11, and 33. Notice that neither 20 nor 33 is itself a prime number.

square number A number that is a result of the product of a number multiplied by itself. For example, 9 and 64 are square numbers because 9 = 3 × 3 and 64 = 8 × 8. A square number represents a number of square tiles that can be arranged to form a square.

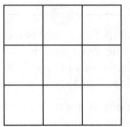

Venn diagram A diagram in which overlapping circles are used to show relationships among sets of objects that have certain attributes. Two examples are shown below.

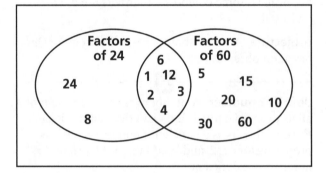

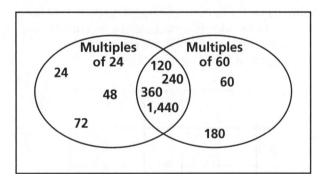

Index

INDEX

Acknowledgments

Team Credits

The people who made up the **Connected Mathematics 2** team—representing editorial, editorial services, design services, and production services—are listed below. Bold type denotes core team members.

Leora Adler, Judith Buice, Kerry Cashman, Patrick Culleton, Sheila DeFazio, Richard Heater, **Barbara Hollingdale, Jayne Holman,** Karen Holtzman, **Etta Jacobs,** Christine Lee, Carolyn Lock, Catherine Maglio, **Dotti Marshall,** Rich McMahon, Eve Melnechuk, Kristin Mingrone, Terri Mitchell, **Marsha Novak,** Irene Rubin, Donna Russo, Robin Samper, Siri Schwartzman, **Nancy Smith,** Emily Soltanoff, **Mark Tricca,** Paula Vergith, Roberta Warshaw, Helen Young

Additional Credits

Diana Bonfilio, Mairead Reddin, Michael Torocsik, nSight, Inc.

Technical Illustration

Seven Worldwide

Cover Design

tom white.images